The World of ELEMENTARY PARTICLES

A BLAISDELL SCIENTIFIC PAPERBACK

BERNARD T. FELD, Massachusetts Institute of Technology

BRENTON F. STEARNS, Tufts University

Consulting Editors

KENNETH W. FORD

The world of
ELEMENTARY
PARTICLES

BLAISDELL PUBLISHING COMPANY

New York • Toronto • London

A DIVISION OF GINN AND COMPANY

First Edition, 1963
Second Printing, 1965

Library of Congress Catalog Card Number: 63-8923
Manufactured in the United States of America

To
PAUL *and* SARAH

Foreword

This is a book of ideas, not of techniques. It is an effort to present the modern scientist's view of the world as shaped by the discoveries of twentieth-century physics, especially in the realm of the very small. Some key experiments are described, but for the most part discussions of the highly complex techniques now employed to study the subatomic domain of nature have deliberately been omitted in order to concentrate on the structure of theories and ideas which comprise our present level of understanding on this fundamental frontier of physical science. To do justice to the elaborate and wonderful apparatus used to extract from nature information about the elementary particle world would require a separate book—one which ought to be written!

I ask the reader to keep in mind two things while reading this book. First, physics is an experimental science. Every theory, every concept, and every picture of nature is based ultimately on experimental findings—what *does* happen in nature. The abstractions and mental constructs have no other aim than to encompass experimental findings in a simple and satisfying way.

The second thing to keep in mind is that every "explanation" of the facts of nature is necessarily provisional. Successful theories are rarely proved incorrect; they are rather shown to be of limited scope and are superseded by more general theories. Therefore, relatively few of the statements of fact in this book are likely to be later proved wrong. But the *view* of the world, the mental picture of nature's activity at the deepest level, to which present-day theory has led us may be radically revised by a new theory. It would not be surprising to see this happen within the next few decades. This book is a progress report, not a statement of final truths about nature.

Many teachers and colleagues have contributed in some measure to this book. In particular, I am indebted to John A. Wheeler, under whose guidance I first came to feel at home in the world of elementary particles; and to Brenton Stearns and Bernard Feld who read the manuscript carefully and made many useful suggestions.

I am grateful also to Silvan Schweber and Stephan Berko for helpful comments. Factual information has generously been supplied by numerous colleagues, including Saul Barshay, Norman Glendenning, Cyrus Gordon, Frederick Reines, Arthur Rosenfeld, Caldwell Titcomb, and David Wilkinson.

Photographs appearing in the book have kindly been furnished by the following individuals or laboratories.

Figure 1.1 (left), Alan Thorndike, Brookhaven National Laboratory.

Figure 1.1 (right), Irwin Pless, Massachusetts Institute of Technology.

Figure 1.2 (left), Carl D. Anderson, California Institute of Technology.

Figure 1.2 (right), Herbert Bridge, Massachusetts Institute of Technology.

Figure 1.4, Joanne B. Ford, with the permission of Brookhaven National Laboratory.

Figure 1.7, Lawrence Radiation Laboratory, University of California.

Figure 1.8, Lawrence Radiation Laboratory, University of California.

Figure 3.2, Irwin Pless, Massachusetts Institute of Technology.

Figure 3.4, M. Françon, Institut d'Optique, Paris.

Figure 4.3, Lawrence Radiation Laboratory, University of California.

Figure 5.3, Jack Steinberger, Columbia University.

Figure 6.2, Irwin Pless, Massachusetts Institute of Technology.

Figure 6.3, Irwin Pless, Massachusetts Institute of Technology.

Figure 6.4, Lawrence Radiation Laboratory, University of California.

Figure 1.2 (left) appeared first in Physical Review, Volume 43, 1933; page 492. Figure 5.3 (lower right) appeared first in Physical Review Letters, Volume 9, 1962, page 40.

The human lifetime figures in the footnote on page 55 were supplied by the John Hancock Mutual Life Insurance Company.

I thank the residents of 94D Cromwell Road, London, where most of this book was written, for providing a pleasant working environment. For encouraging the creation of this book and for reading the manuscript I am especially grateful to my wife Joanne.

Kenneth W. Ford

Contents

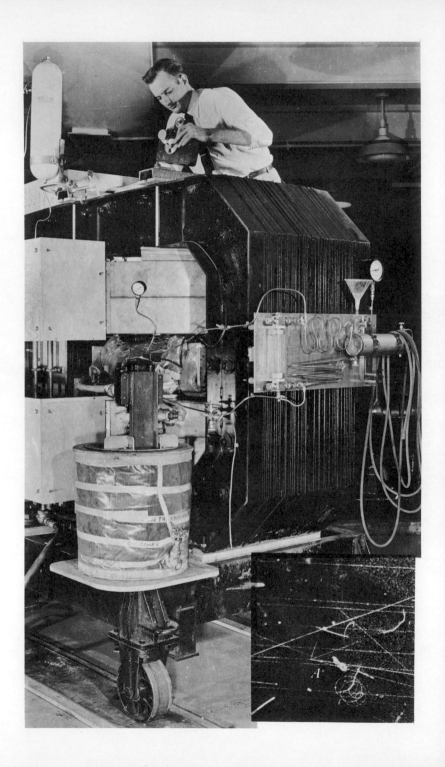

Figure 1.1. Particle detectors and particle tracks. The photograph on the opposite page shows a 16-inch cloud chamber housed within a powerful electromagnet at the Brookhaven National Laboratory, New York. On this page is the 15-inch bubble chamber of the Cambridge (Massachusetts) Bubble Chamber Group. The insets are photographs of tracks left in these chambers by high-speed elementary particles. At the left, one of many protons flying through the cloud chamber collides with an atomic nucleus at point A and produces two new particles (pions). A beam of many pions produced most of the tracks above; this photograph is reproduced and interpreted later as Figure 6.3.

In passing through matter at high speed, an electrified particle such as a proton or pion disrupts one atom after another in its path, leaving behind a trail of electrically charged atoms, called ions. In the gas-filled cloud chamber, these ions act as centers of condensation for vapor contained in the gas. A line of liquid droplets marks the path of the particle through the gas. (The visible moisture of ordinary clouds in the air consists in part also of droplets centered about ions.) In the liquid-filled bubble chamber, on the other hand, the particle path is traced by a line of gas bubbles. The ions in the wake of the particle act as centers of boiling in the superheated liquid of the bubble chamber. An instant after the bubbles form, before the boiling initiated along the track has had a chance to spread throughout the liquid, the photograph is taken.

Chapter One

The Elementary-Particle Zoo

When a jet plane passes high overhead, the cloud of ice crystals formed in its trail is clearly visible even when the airplane itself can not be seen. It is a piece of good luck for man that the smallest objects he knows anything about—the bits of matter and energy he calls elementary particles—behave in a similar way. A single elementary particle is over ten million times smaller than the smallest thing that can be seen under a microscope. Yet when the particle flies at high speed through a cloud chamber or through the more modern bubble chamber, it leaves in its wake a trail visible to the naked eye; this trail can be photographed and studied at leisure (see Figure 1.1). The particle may also leave its mark directly in specially prepared photographic film, or may record its presence by triggering an electronic counter.

The remaining and still very formidable task facing the modern physicist is to reconstruct, from the trails and from the clicks of counters, the nature of the elementary particles. This is roughly like reconstructing the design of a jet plane by studying its high-altitude wake. It is the effort to elucidate the mysteries of the elementary particles which has led to the construction of enormous accelerators, to the design of clever and complicated experiments employing every known technological refinement, and to a concerted theoretical and mathematical attack.

We have learned a great deal about the elementary particles in recent years—enough to catalogue different species, to know the intrinsic properties of each, to learn something about the interaction of one kind of particle with another, and to begin to see a glimmer of nature's design at this submicroscopic level. But, in the ways that matter most to the scientist, we know very little. There is no over-all theory accounting for the whys of the particles: why there are as many as there are (and there is good reason to believe they have not all been discovered yet); why they have the masses

1

they do; why they are born, live, interact, and die as they do (most of them have a life span of less than one millionth of a second).

The elementary particles are not just interesting scientific curiosities. They represent the deepest-lying substructure of matter to which man has been able to probe; consequently, they provide one of the most challenging problems on the current frontiers of science. The faith which has been the most powerful stimulus to scientific progress throughout history—the faith in the underlying simplicity of nature—provides the motivation to continue the search for a theory to explain the elementary particles. Most scientists believe, with the weight of history on their side, that some day soon the collection of different particles with different properties will fall into a simple and orderly pattern and clear the way for advance to a still deeper domain of nature.

This book will be devoted mainly to recounting what we do know about the particles and what the particles have taught us about nature. (We shall often omit the modifier "elementary," which is very likely unjustified anyway.) Our account will also indicate why we think there is much more to learn and will place the particles in perspective with the rest of physical science. The particles have generated a great deal of excitement in the world of science; perhaps this book will succeed also in imparting a little of that excitement to the reader.

Much of the history of science can be characterized as a probing away from the world of man's immediate sense experience (the so-called macroscopic world), upward to the cosmological world and downward to the submicroscopic world. The elementary particles represent the present-day limit of the downward probing. The view of the world as a structure built of units which are, in turn, built of smaller units, and so on downward (a view by no means necessary, but quite successful) makes the world of the very small appear to be the most fundamental frontier of science.

Man and the familiar objects of his world are constructed from atoms and molecules. At the turn of this century, atoms were known to exist but, as with today's elementary particles, the structure of the atom and the relation of one atom to another was a mystery. It was known that the atom was the smallest unit of an element such as hydrogen or oxygen or sodium or uranium; that there were something over eighty different kinds of atoms (today we know just over a hundred); and that atoms were all of about the same size, such that one hundred million of them side by side would stretch into a line less than one inch long. It was also known that groups of different kinds of atoms could join together to form tiny structures called molecules, which, in turn, became the basic building blocks of the vast and wonderful variety of substances we encounter in the world. The simplest molecules contain very few atoms. A molecule of table salt, sodium chloride, contains just two, one sodium atom and one chlorine atom; a molecule of water, which everyone knows is H_2O, is made of two hydrogen atoms and one oxygen atom. Some complicated molecules such as the proteins in living matter contain many thousands of atoms.

In the first decade of the twentieth century discoveries came thick and fast, leading to a giant step downward toward the sub-atomic world of particles. The electron, the first known particle, had been discovered in 1897; it was suspected to be a particle contained within atoms. As a common constituent of atoms, it provided a link between distinct atoms. Another important link was forged when, in 1902, it was discovered that a radioactive atom (one capable of spontaneously emitting powerful radiation) could transmute itself into an entirely different kind of atom. This transmutation strongly suggested that atoms must be not indepen-dent, indivisible entities, but structures built up of some common, more elementary building blocks.

The alpha particles ejected at high speed from radioactive atoms were used shortly thereafter as the first projectiles for bombard-ing atoms. (These atomic "bullets," conveniently provided free by nature, are not energetic enough for modern purposes; today they are replaced by particles artificially pushed to still higher speeds in giant accelerators.) A result of the early bombardments was the revelation that the interior of atoms is largely empty space. By 1911 the experimenter Ernest Rutherford had discovered that the atom contained a massive, positively charged core—the nucleus —at least ten thousand times smaller than the atom as a whole, and that the remaining space was occupied by a few light-weight, nega-tively charged electrons. Two years later the theorist Niels Bohr provided a successful mathematical description of the motion of the electrons in the atom. Despite later modifications of detail, this description remains, in its essentials, our picture of atomic structure up to the present. The electrons whirl rapidly about the nucleus providing a sort of atomic skin, just as a whirling propeller seems to form a disk. Like a bullet which passed safely between the propeller blades of a World War I fighter plane, a high-speed particle can readily penetrate the electron cloud to reach deep within the atom. Another atom, however, drifting up with a relatively low speed, is turned back at the periphery, much as a stone tossed slowly at a spinning propeller might be batted back.

The nucleus of the lightest atom, hydrogen, was christened the proton and joined the electron to bring the list of elementary particles of fifty years ago up to two. Heavier nuclei were believed to be formed of a number of protons and electrons packed closely together. The details of this picture of nuclear structure were never clear; indeed, it was abandoned in 1932. However, it was a most attractive idea to have just two fundamental particles—the negatively charged electron and the positively charged proton—from which all of the matter in the universe was constructed. The only puzzling feature (a puzzle not yet resolved) was why the proton should be much heavier than the electron. In any case, this idyllic two-particle situation was not to last.

Several things happened in the early 1930's to begin the disturbing increase in the number of known elementary particles which has continued until the present time. A new particle, the neutron, was discovered; it was about as massive as the proton but carried no electric charge. The neutron was quite welcome, for it was just the particle needed to join the proton to form atomic nuclei. The picture of the nucleus immediately adopted and still accepted was that of a collection of protons and neutrons glued tightly together by a new strong force, simply called the nuclear force. For example, U^{235}, the most famous isotope of uranium, has a nucleus consisting of 92 protons and 143 neutrons. The far simpler nucleus of helium (the same thing as an alpha particle) contains two neutrons and two protons.

At nearly the same time, a fourth particle was discovered by the track it left in a cloud chamber exposed to cosmic radiation in Pasadena, California. This new particle, the positron, was as light as the electron but carried a positive instead of a negative charge. Some positron tracks are shown in Figure 1.2. Like the neutron, the positron arrived at an opportune time. A few years earlier, in 1928, Paul Dirac had constructed a new theory of the electron which was brilliantly successful in accounting for the fine details of atomic structure. But Dirac's theory seemed to have one flaw. It predicted a sister particle for the electron, alike in all respects except the sign of its electric charge. A slot in the structure of theoretical physics was ready and waiting for the positron when Carl Anderson discovered it in 1932. (Dirac's theory also predicted a negatively charged sister for the proton, called the antiproton, but many years had to go by before it was seen. The construction of the six-billion-volt Bevatron in Berkeley, California, made possible the production of antiprotons and they were first observed in Berkeley in 1955.)

The advance of physical theory in the early 1930's led finally to the "rediscovery" of an old particle, the photon. Back in 1905, the same year his first important paper on relativity was published, Albert Einstein had shown that a phenomenon called the photoelectric effect (which will be discussed in Chapter Five) could best be understood with the assumption that light waves are absorbed only in bundles of a definite size. These energy packets, now called photons, behaved in some ways like particles, yet were quite different from ordinary material particles. Although they carried energy, they had no mass. They could be neither speeded up nor slowed down, but traveled always at the same invariable (and enormous) speed. They could be born and die (that is, be emitted and absorbed), whereas ordinary particles—or so it was then believed—remained in existence forever. And, unlike material particles, the photon could never be isolated at a particular point except during the moment of its birth or death; otherwise it spread in a diffuse manner through space. For all of these reasons, the photon was not associated with the electron and the proton as a true elementary particle.

The quantum theory, discovered in 1925 and developed over the next decade, changed this view of the photon. It showed that, from a fundamental point of view, the difference between a photon and a material particle was not so great. The particle happened to have mass; the photon did not. All of their other dissimilarities could simply be understood as arising from this single difference. In particular, the quantum theory suggested that it should be possible for material particles to be created and annihilated. The photon appeared not to be so distinctive after all and it joined the list of elementary particles.

Very shortly a theory developed by Enrico Fermi showed that

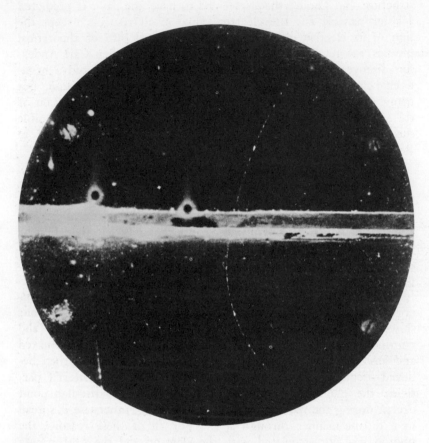

Figure 1.2. Positron tracks. On the left is Carl Anderson's photograph which first served to identify the positron in 1932. Entering the chamber at the top, the positron is deflected into a curved path by a magnetic force. After being slowed down in the central metal plate, it is more strongly deflected. An electron trajectory would have curved in the opposite direction. On the right is a more recent cloud-chamber photograph of a "shower" containing a multitude of positrons and electrons, as well as invisible photons. A high-energy photon can create simultaneously an electron and a positron. These particles, in turn, emit photons which create further electron-positron pairs, and so on, like a cascade of fireworks until the shower finally dissipates its energy. In the right-hand picture, there is no magnetic force and the particles fly in straight lines.

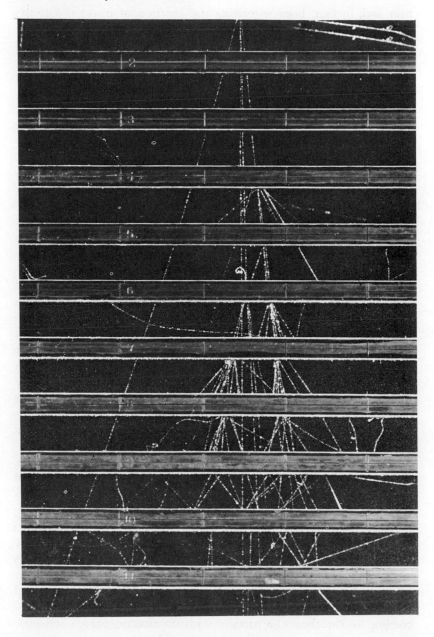

Figure 1.2. (Continued).

man had, in fact, been witnessing the creation of material particles for some time. Ever since early studies of radioactivity at the beginning of this century, scientists had known that some radioactive atoms shoot out high-speed electrons which, in this particular manifestation, were called beta particles. The radioactive transformation giving rise to these electrons was known as beta decay, but its revolutionary import was not suspected for many years. Since atoms were known to contain electrons, it did not seem surprising that electrons should sometimes be ejected from atoms. Even after the discovery of the atomic nucleus in 1911, when it became clear that the beta electrons must emerge from the nucleus, the significance of beta decay was not appreciated. Electrons were simply assumed to exist within the nucleus as well as in the space surrounding the nucleus. But when the discovery of the neutron in 1932, together with various theoretical difficulties, finally banished electrons from the nucleus, beta decay became perplexing. Fermi in 1934 suggested that, at the instant of the radioactive transformation, an electron came suddenly into existence in the nucleus and swiftly departed to be recorded as the beta particle. In short, beta decay, already known for many years, represented the creation of material particles. Fermi's suggestion was, of course, more than a verbal hypothesis. Couched in mathematical language within the framework of the quantum theory, it gave a satisfying explanation of beta decay. Among other things, it predicted the possibility that the beta transformation might, for some atoms, result in positrons rather than electrons; this was later verified with artificially produced radioactive materials. Only slightly modified, Fermi's theory still gives an adequate explanation of all beta-decay phenomena.

As so often happens with successful theories in physical science, there is an unexpected bonus. The theory does what is expected of it and then a bit more. Dirac's theory of the electron magnificently explained details of atomic structure and then surprisingly predicted the positron as well. Fermi's theory, in a similar way, accounted for beta decay and as a bonus predicted a strange new particle, the neutrino. (The first prediction of the neutrino was actually made by Wolfgang Pauli several years before Fermi's work. More accurately stated, Fermi provided a definite mathematical framework to accommodate Pauli's speculative suggestion.) According to the theory, a particle with no electric charge and little or no mass (it is now believed to be, like the photon, precisely massless) is also created at the moment of beta decay and leaves the nucleus along with the electron. This most elusive of all particles leaves no trail in a cloud chamber and travels through miles of solid material as if nothing were there. Nevertheless, theory demanded it as a new member of the elementary-particle family and physicists would have been most upset if the neutrino had not finally been detected. The story of its observation in 1956 and the discovery of a second kind of neutrino in 1962 is left to Chapter Five.

By the middle 1930's the electron and the proton had been joined by the photon, the neutron, and the positron (or antielectron). The neutrino, although not directly observed, was a theoretical necessity, and was added with considerable confidence to the list of particles. In addition, there was every reason to believe that antiprotons and antineutrons existed.

Before most scientists all over the world left their fundamental research to devote their talents to the technology of warfare, two more particles were predicted and one more particle was discovered (which was neither of the predicted particles). In a brilliant piece of theoretical work in Japan in 1935, Hideki Yukawa predicted the particle we now call the pi meson or pion. For this he was awarded a Nobel prize—after his prediction proved to be correct. Yukawa initiated a line of reasoning about the nature of forces which has become one of the key steps in the transition from our "everyday" way of looking at the world to the new way of looking at the submicroscopic world.

Force is a familiar idea in our daily life. It is a push or a pull, usually seeming to be associated with physical contact. The seat of your chair exerts a force to hold you up. If you bump into another pedestrian on the sidewalk, you feel a force pushing you aside. The tires of a car exert a force on the road to push the car forward, and if the contact between tire and road is not firm enough (as on an icy pavement), not enough force can be exerted. But we also know of forces which act without direct contact. A comb run through the hair on a dry day can attract a bit of paper without touching it. Two magnets brought close together can push or pull each other without contact. Moreover, if we think on an atomic scale, the idea of contact—of touching—becomes ill defined. In the collision between two pedestrians, the atoms in the coat sleeve of one run up against the atoms in the coat sleeve of the other. But an atom has no well-defined boundary; it is a fuzzy-edged object. It is impossible to say whether two atoms are touching or not touching. One can only say that two atoms close together exert forces on each other and two atoms far apart feel little or no force.

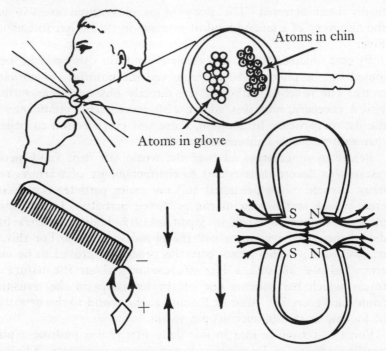

Atoms in chin

Atoms in glove

Figure 1.3. The nature of forces. The apparent contact force between boxer's glove and chin is really "action at a distance." Different groups of atoms exert forces on each other over an intervening space just as an electrified comb attracts a bit of paper or two magnets push on each other without direct contact. All three of the forces pictured here are basically electrical in nature and arise from the rapid exchange of photons.

By the middle of the nineteenth century scientists had given up the naive idea of force through contact and replaced it by "action at a distance" (see Figure 1.3). The force of gravity acts over vast stretches of empty space. The electric force of comb on paper and the magnetic force between magnets require no physical contact. Even the normal contact forces—between a boxer's glove and his opponent's chin, for instance—can be understood as forces acting over a distance (true, an uncomfortably short distance) between different collections of atoms. A new entity, the "field," was invented to explain *why* forces can act through empty space, but we shall save our discussion of fields for Chapter Seven.

A few years after the discovery of quantum mechanics, and just before Yukawa's work, a quantum theory of electric and magnetic forces was developed. This theory, which was responsible for the new view of the photon as an elementary particle, assigned to the photon the role of carrier of the force. A proton and an electron, for example (which attract each other electrically), continually exchange photons. Each electrically charged particle is continually emitting and absorbing photons, and it is this ceaseless exchange which gives rise to the force. Just how the exchange produces a force can not really be visualized, but a crude analogy might help. A solitary charged particle sends out and then recaptures photons like a boy batting out a ball attached to a rubber cord which draws the ball back to him after each blow. If he is approached by another boy engaged in the same sport, each might "absorb" the ball of the other, that is, reach out and grab the other's ball as it approaches. The rubber cords would then tend to pull the boys together; in other words, the exchange would produce an attractive force. This is about as close as one can come to visualizing the process of exchanging photons; but it is not very close. In truth, photons are not attached to anything, and their exchange may give rise either to a repulsive or to an attractive force. In any case, the quantum theory of photon exchange initiated a revolutionary new understanding of the nature of electric force (and of the closely related magnetic force).

Yukawa gave thought to the powerful new nuclear force that acted between the nuclear particles, protons and neutrons, to hold them together in the tiny nuclei within atoms. He asked the question: What if this force also arises from an exchange between the nuclear particles? The thing exchanged, he demonstrated, could not be a photon, nor could it be any other known particle. (Yukawa's reasoning, which rests on basic ideas in the quantum theory, will be explained in Chapter Six.) The new particle should be 200 to 300 times more massive than an electron (but still six to nine times lighter than a proton). A dozen years elapsed before the Yukawa particle was finally discovered, first in cosmic radiation in 1947, and the following year in the debris from nuclear collisions in an accelerator in Berkeley, California. This particle, now called the pion, is today a very well-known member of the elementary-particle zoo. It is 274 times more massive than the electron, and there is little doubt that it is the intermediate particle primarily responsible for nuclear forces.

The Yukawa view that all forces arise from the exchange of intermediate particles led to the prediction of another new particle, the graviton. Gravity, since it holds the solar system together, is very obviously a long-range force. It is, like the electric force, of infinite range; therefore, the particles whose exchange gives rise to the gravitational force must be, like photons, massless. These as yet unobserved particles have been christened gravitons, and we know their properties, even though they have never been detected. The chances of direct observation of gravitons in the foreseeable future are indeed slim because of the weakness of the gravitational force—by far the weakest force known to man. This assertion may seem surprising. Anyone who has struggled up a 14,000-foot peak or has broken a leg skiing might well claim that the gravitational force is the strongest force with which he has had to contend. The resolution of this paradox—that the force we are all most aware of in everyday life is the weakest in nature—is postponed to Chapter Five.

Not long after the pion and the graviton were predicted, the muon was discovered. This discovery roughly marks the beginning of the chaotic period in elementary-particle physics which extends to the present—the period during which unexpected particles have kept appearing on the scene. The muon's trail was first identified beyond question in cloud-chamber photographs of cosmic radiation in 1936; its properties came slowly into focus over the next decade. With a mass about 200 times that of the electron, at first the muon looked like the Yukawa particle. Gradually, however, it became clear that the muon could not play the role that Yukawa had written into the drama of science. His hypothesized particle, being responsible for nuclear forces, should interact strongly with nuclei. The muon, on the contrary, was indifferent to nuclei, responding electrically to the proton's charge, but otherwise penetrating nuclei as if they were not there. Today we know the muon's properties with remarkable accuracy, but its place in the scheme of nature remains a mystery.

The collection of known particles expanded rapidly between 1947 and 1954 with the discovery of four more groups whose members are known collectively as "strange" particles (the physicist's straightforward way of confessing his mystification about these unexpected particles). The kaons (or K particles) constitute the lightest of the new groups, each kaon being about half as heavy as a proton; each of the other strange particles, consisting of the groups of lambda (Λ), sigma (Σ), and xi (Ξ) particles, is somewhat heavier than a proton. These particles were all seen first in cosmic radiation. Studies of their properties are now in progress at the sites of high-energy accelerators: Geneva, Switzerland; Brookhaven, New York; Berkeley, California; and Dubna, U. S. S. R. The Brookhaven machine is shown in Figure 1.4.

Before the construction of these accelerators, physicists had to rely exclusively on cosmic radiation as a source of particles. Luckily, the earth is continually bombarded by particles from outer space, enough to provide the physicist with particles to study, but not enough to be a health hazard to the world's population sheltered beneath the blanket of air. Most of the particles are protons, some of which have exceedingly great energy. When the protons strike the air nuclear collisions occur, giving rise to a shower of various particles, including the short-lived muons, pions, and strange particles, as well as photons, electrons, and positrons. It was through cloud chambers exposed to cosmic radiation that most of the known particles were discovered. But the physicist carrying out particle experiments with the random cosmic radiation is about like an aeronautical engineer mounting a wing to be tested in an open field and hoping a high wind will spring up. As the engineer turns to the controlled conditions of a wind tunnel, the physicist has turned to the controlled conditions of the beams of particles accelerated in high-energy machines. Only for studying processes at energies beyond any yet reached by machines does he now return to the cosmic radiation.

The need for machines the size of a football field to study the tiniest things in nature is a paradox related to two remarkable connecting links discovered in this century: the connection between mass and energy, and the connection between waves and particles. These subtle connections, which have so strongly altered man's

Figure 1.4. For descriptive legend see page 15.

view of the small-scale world, will be elucidated in Chapters Two and Three.

For the most part, physicists seeking new particles have been like trappers in an unfamiliar forest. They set out their cloud chambers and other detectors and wait in suspense to see what might wander into them. But in 1962 a second kind of neutrino was deliberately sought and found, proving the worth of the big new accelerators. Neutrinos cannot be created alone; they are born only in conjunction with other particles. The neutrino of Pauli and Fermi is a partner of the electron; the muon also has its neutrino partner. Once the Brookhaven accelerator, pictured in Figure 1.4, was in operation, it became possible to answer the question: Are these two neutrinos the same? The answer was no, and one more member of the elementary-particle zoo was captured and classified.

Although the controlled conditions of the modern accelerator make possible searches for specific particles such as the muon's neutrino, the suspense and uncertainty are far from removed. There have been unexpected surprises too; recent experiments with the new machines have revealed a whole new class of super-short-lived particles. These particles come into existence and vanish again so quickly that they cannot move a noticeable distance and they leave no direct record of their presence. Most of the "old-fashioned" particles live long enough to move at least a few centimeters—an enormous distance on the submicroscopic scale—and to leave a track in a cloud chamber or a bubble chamber. The new particles are detected only by more indirect means, and lead to the semiphilosophical question: When is a particle a particle? Some people

---

Figure 1.4. The Alternating Gradient Synchrotron at Brookhaven, New York. Protons are guided magnetically around the 840-foot diameter "racetrack" in a partially buried tunnel as they are pushed to higher and higher energy. In less than one second, a proton completes over three-hundred thousand circuits of the track before reaching its peak energy of thirty-three billion electron volts. Altogether the machine provides some seven thousand billion high-energy protons per minute for use as projectiles in elementary-particle research. At the top is an air view of the AGS, visible only as a doughnut-shaped mound. The lower photograph shows a series of magnets enclosing the proton-beam tube as it arcs through the experimental building. (Dust covers are in place during a period of maintenance.)

prefer to call these new ephemeral particles "resonances." Whatever they are called it seems clear that they are elementary structures closely related to the structures generally called particles which happen to be dignified by longer lives. Nevertheless, in the interest of avoiding complication, we shall usually ignore these newly discovered objects, which, as this book is being written, are only beginning to be understood. What little is now known of them will be discussed in Chapter Six.

Although the number of elementary particles is disturbingly large to the theorist seeking a simple explanation of their structure and their interconnections, it is still a manageably small number, smaller, say, than the number of different atoms known in 1900. Table 1 lists the names and the identifying characteristics of every known species in the elementary-particle zoo (excluding the resonances). Since it will be convenient to refer to Table 1 from time to time in later chapters, it is placed at the back of the book on a pull-out sheet. (On the inner part of the same sheet is a Greek alphabet as a helpful guide to the symbols which have come into common use in designating the particles.) The remainder of this chapter will be devoted mainly to discussion of some of those properties listed in the table which serve to distinguish one particle from another.

In Table 1, the number of different kinds of particles known with certainty is thirteen, or, if we include the graviton whose existence is so strongly suspected, fourteen. Certain very closely related particles are lumped together. The electron and its antiparticle, the positron, for example, are of the same kind. The neutron and proton are also united under one heading, the nucleon (so named because protons and neutrons are the constituents of nuclei), along with their opposites, the antiproton and the antineutron. The number of distinct individual particles, not counting the graviton, is thirty-five.

Perhaps the most important identifying characteristic of a particle is its mass. The photon, the graviton, and the neutrinos are massless. Having no mass is the same as having no inertia, that is, having no resistance to being speeded up; consequently, the massless particles always move as fast as it is possible to move, at nature's speed limit, the invariable speed of light (which could therefore just as well be called the speed of gravity or the speed of neutrinos). The lightest particle with mass is the electron (and the equally massive positron); its mass therefore provides a convenient unit for weighing in the other particles. Next comes the muon, more than two hundred times heavier than the electron. The pion is somewhat heavier than the muon (but close enough to explain why the muon, when first discovered, was mistaken for the pion). The list continues on to the heaviest known "elementary" particle, the omega, with a mass 3280 times greater than that of the electron. There are, of course, heavier known particles, nuclei, atoms, molecules, or a speck of dirt in the eye. But all of these are understood as composites of two or more of those listed in Table 1. The omega particle is the heaviest particle which might be elementary, since it has not yet been explained as a composite of any of the lighter particles. That *all* of these particles are built up from some more primordial material remains, of course, a strong possibility.

The Dirac theory of the electron first predicted that a particle should be accompanied in nature by a sister particle, identical in mass, but opposite in electric charge and in some other intrinsic properties. This sister particle is usually called an antiparticle (although it is itself a perfectly good particle), and it appears that every particle in nature has its antiparticle. (The antiparticle of the antiparticle is the original particle.) For the special cases of the photon, the graviton, the neutral pion, and the eta, the antiparticle is the same as the particle, but for all other members of the zoo, particle and antiparticle differ. The antineutron, for example, is distinguishable from the neutron, even though both are neutral. The proton and antiproton are even more easily distinguishable, since one is positively charged, the other negatively charged. A horizontal bar over a particle symbol is used to designate the antiparticle.

The fact that particle-antiparticle pairs exist in nature was a startling and unexpected consequence of merging the theory of relativity and the theory of quantum mechanics. It is scarcely possible to describe in words how that came about. Relativity is a kind of legalistic theory which imposes its rules on all other theories. "Lesser" theories (for example, quantum mechanics) must satisfy the rule that experimenters carrying out the same measurements in different frames of reference must get the same results. It was found impossible to construct a theory of single particles which conformed to this invariance requirement of relativity. Only if antiparticles were admitted as well could the laws of relativity be satisfied. It is rather as if you were given a set of identical colored strips like those pictured in Figure 1.5, red on one side, green on the other, and were asked to construct from them any designs whatever, subject only to the invariance requirement that the completed design should appear the same to a man who could see only red as to a man who could see only green. It would not take long for you to discover the impossibility of this task unless you were also furnished with some "antistrips" like those in Figure 1.6. In a similar way, particles alone proved to be insufficient to construct a relativistic theory; antiparticles were needed as well. There is now ample evidence for antiparticles and their existence gives support to both

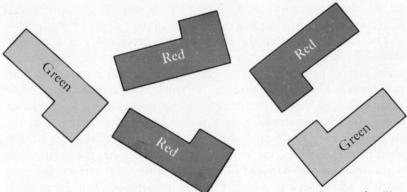

Figure 1.5. Colored strips, which alone cannot be used to make "invariant" designs whose red parts and green parts appear identical.

the theories of relativity and of quantum mechanics. Figure 1.7 is an interesting photograph showing an antilambda and two antiprotons.

A fascinating property possessed by most of the particles is spin. This means that each particle is spinning about an axis like a top, but forever, at an invariable rate, characteristic of the particle. There is actually no way to tell how fast a particle is spinning. The "amount" of its spin can not be measured in terms of revolutions per minute, but must be measured in units of angular momentum. Angular momentum is a somewhat more complicated quantity, depending not only on speed of rotation but also on the mass and on the size of the rotating object. We shall not give an exact definition, but note that more speed, or more mass, or greater size, or any combination of increases of these quantities produces greater angular momentum. A spinning electron has a certain angular momentum; a spinning top has much more because it is vastly bigger and heavier; a spinning merry-go-round has still more, even though its rate of turning is lower. Angular momentum can be thought of as the strength of rotation and it is related to the effort required to start or stop the rotational motion.

Spin in the submicroscopic world is conveniently measured in units of the photon spin, given in the table simply as 1. The electron

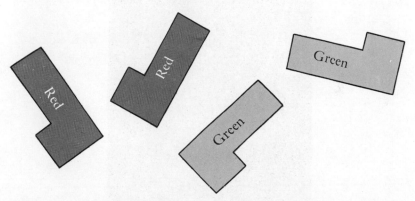

Figure 1.6. "Antistrips." These are needed, as well as the strips in Figure 1.5, in order to construct color-invariant designs, just as both particles and antiparticles are needed to construct a properly invariant theory of nature.

has a spin of ½; that is, it has half as much rotational angular momentum as a photon. A few particles, such as pions, have no spin at all. Except for the graviton, predicted to have spin 2, all of the particles have spin 0, ½, or 1.

According to the quantum theory, some physical quantities can take on only distinct, separated values ("discrete values," in the language of mathematics) and angular momentum is one of these. If the same type of law applied, say, to speed in the everyday world, one might have a car which could travel only at 10 miles per hour, or at 20, or at 30, but not at any intermediate speed. This would make traveling rather jerky. Indeed the quantum theory gives to the submicroscopic world just such a jerkiness; physical

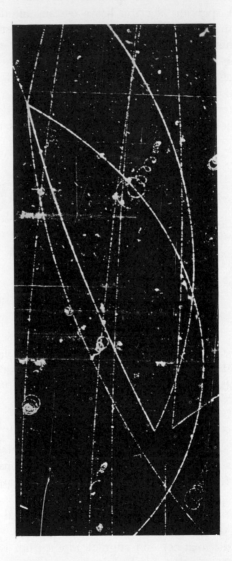

Figure 1.7. Particles and antiparticles. An antiproton entering the bubble chamber at the bottom vanishes in collision with a proton in the chamber, giving rise, in a rare event, to a lambda-antilambda pair. These neutral particles leave no tracks, but decay into charged particles which do. One of the products of the antilambda decay is another antiproton

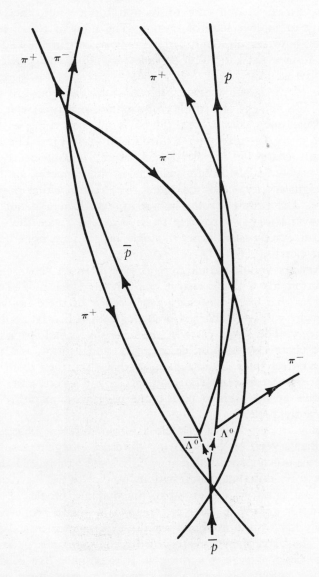

whose annihilation in the upper left part of the chamber produces a spray of pions. This is the more usual result of the collision between an antiproton and a proton. Because the chamber is in a magnetic field, positive particles are deflected in one direction, negative particles in the other direction.

systems remain in one state of motion for a while, then change suddenly to another state of motion. The spins of the elementary particles, however, although pegged only at certain allowed values, remain forever fixed for each particle (as long as that particle continues to exist).

Some of the particles possess electric charge, some are neutral. Charge, like spin, is one of those quantities in nature which come in packages of a certain size. There is no such thing as half an electron charge or three and a third electron charges. The amount of electric charge on the electron is nature's unit of electricity. In fact, every other elementary particle is either neutral or has the same magnitude of electric charge as the electron, either positive or negative. The reason for this is not known. It would not violate any known laws for a particle to have exactly twice the electron charge, or exactly three times as much; but, in fact, none has more than the electron.

A given species of particle may exist in different "charge states." An electron has a single charge state; it is negative. The neutral lambda also has only one charge state. Each of these has an antiparticle, the positively charged positron, and the neutral antilambda, respectively. The sigma particle, the most diversified species, exists in three charge states, positive, negative, and neutral, and to each of these corresponds an antisigma, so that altogether there are six different sigma particles. The pion species is a special case, for the antiparticle of the positive pion is the negative pion rather than a distinct antiparticle.

Roughly, to say that a particle exists in different charge states means that several particles having different charge are so nearly alike in all other respects that it is only logical to regard them as, in some way, different manifestations of the "same" particle. The proton and neutron, for example, the building blocks of atomic nuclei, differ greatly in their electric and magnetic properties, but are nearly identical in mass and seem to experience identical nuclear forces. They are, therefore, regarded as different charge states of the same basic particle, the nucleon. It is roughly like issuing the same basic automobile chassis and engine in two quite different body styles.

The mass of a particle, its charge, and its spin are among its most important identifying features, but these by no means exhaust the properties a particle may have. To know a particle fully one must know how it interacts with each other particle. The interaction properties are not yet fully known, and are the subject of the most intensive investigation.

The most dramatic consequence of particle interaction is the transformation of one kind of particle into two or more other lighter particles. A charged pion, for example, left to itself, will live about two hundredths of one millionth of a second, and then spontaneously vanish, to be replaced most probably by a muon and a neutrino, but possibly by an electron and a neutrino (see Figure 1.8). The pion is said to "decay" into the two lighter particles. Most of the known particles are unstable and decay in a variety of ways after a very short time. Table 1 shows the characteristic lifetimes for the known particles and the typical modes of decay for those which are unstable. Only the proton, the electron, and the massless particles are stable, that is, each has—as far as we know—an infinite lifetime.

Without the stability of the electron and the proton, man would not be on hand to study the elementary particles. The stability of the massless particles is of no value for constructing matter, for the photon, graviton, and neutrinos cannot be corralled and held in one place for use as bricks in the structure of the universe. They fly forever onward at the speed of light. This leaves only the electron and proton as suitable building blocks of the world. In addition, by a stroke of good luck, the neutron can be stabilized when joined with protons. A solitary neutron decays into a proton, an electron and an antineutrino after an average lifetime of about 17 minutes. But when the neutron joins a proton, the attractive force holding them together causes a lowering of the energy of the neutron which, in turn, prohibits its decay. Exactly how this effect, which is dependent on the mass-energy equivalence, comes about will be discussed in Chapter Six. Without this stabilizing effect the world would contain only hydrogen, for the hydrogen atom is the only atom built exclusively of electrons and protons (one of each). The existence of every other substance in the world depends upon the fact that the nuclear forces are powerful enough to stabilize the normally unstable neutron and make it also available as a universal building block.

In view of the incredibly short lifetimes of most of the particles, one may be tempted to ask why they seem to be so important. A

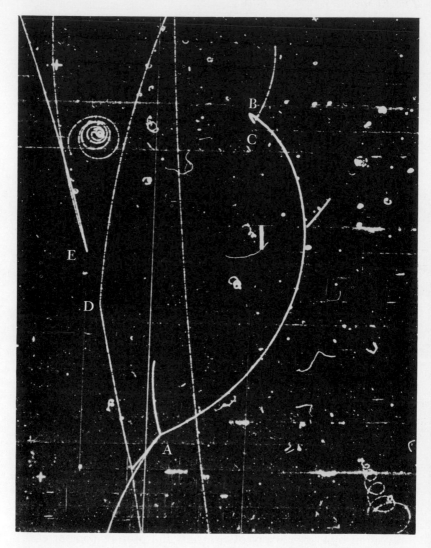

Figure 1.8. Decay of unstable particles. This unusual bubble-chamber photograph shows the decay of five different elementary particles. At point *A*, a positive kaon decays into three pions. At *B*, one of these pions decays into a muon and an unseen neutrino. At *C*, the muon decays into a positron (plus two neutrinos). At point *D*, a xi particle decays into a lambda particle and a pion. The invisible neutral lambda decays into a proton and a pion at point *E*.

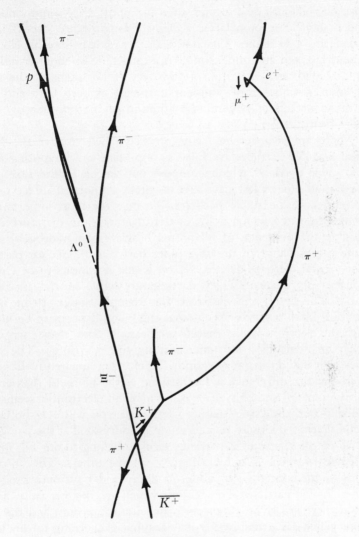

Figure 1.8. (Continued).

proton is obviously important; all matter, animate and inanimate, contains protons. But why a lambda particle, say, which is not a constituent of anything we know? In a sufficiently violent nuclear collision brought about with the help of a man-made accelerator, a lambda particle may be created. It travels a few centimeters in less than one billionth of a second, then promptly decays into a nucleon and a pion. The pion, after a slightly longer time, decays into a muon and a neutrino. The muon decays shortly into an electron, a neutrino, and an antineutrino. In a total time of about a millionth of a second, and all within a few feet of the point of the initial collision, a sequence of transient particles has been born and died, with no net effect beyond the addition to the universe of a few more neutrinos.

There are two reasons why physicists believe that the short-lived unstable particles are fully as important and interesting as the few stable particles which compose our world. In the first place, the unstable particles may have a vitally important effect on the properties of the stable particles. To give the most important example, the force which holds nuclei together (and therefore makes possible the existence of all atoms heavier than hydrogen) arises from the exchange of unstable pions between the nuclear particles. The second, perhaps deeper, reason is that it appears to be entirely a matter of "chance" which particles are stable and which are unstable. The muon and electron, for example, appear to be nearly identical in all respects except that the muon happens to be heavier than the electron. It can therefore release its extra mass energy and decay spontaneously into an electron (and neutrinos). The muon lives two millionths of a second; the electron apparently lives forever. Yet this difference is less striking to the physicist than are the many points of similarity between muon and electron. It seems very unlikely that the "true" nature of the electron will ever be understood unless the closely related muon is understood at the same time.

All of the elementary particles seem to belong to one big family. No one of them is independent of all the others. The "normal" thing is for a particle to undergo decay and transmute itself into other lighter particles. For reasons which are not yet fully understood there are two "abnormal" particles, the proton and the electron, which are prohibited from decaying. According to this larger view of the particles, there are certain rules of nature (see Chapter Four) which happen to prevent the decay of these two particles. Because of this chance, the construction of a material world is possible.

Of course, since there is only one universe, and one set of natural laws, it does not make much sense to say that a particular state of affairs in the world exists by chance. But this view of the multiplicity of particles continues the process, begun by Copernicus, of making man feel more and more humble when facing the design of nature. We and our world exist by the grace of certain conservation laws which stabilize a few particles and permit an orderly structure to be built upon the normal chaos of the submicroscopic world.

Table 1 contains one more piece of information, the classification of particles into family groups: the baryons (heavy particles), the mesons (intermediate particles), and the muon and electron families. The muon, the electron, and their respective neutrinos, which comprise the last two families, are also known as leptons (light particles). The pion, kaon, and eta are mesons. The proton and all heavier particles—neutron through omega—are the baryons. These words of Greek origin do much more than label particles according to their mass. Note in Table 1, for example, that the leptons and baryons have spin $\frac{1}{2}$, while the mesons have spin 0. More important, the groups deserve to be separated and given family names because there are laws of conservation for three of the four families. Whenever one baryon disappears, another one appears in its place. It is the law of baryon conservation that stabilizes the proton. The proton cannot decay into any lighter particles because it is itself the lightest baryon and such a decay would require the disappearance of a baryon with no replacement. Similar laws apply to the muon family and to the electron family, but not to the mesons, which, like photons, can be created and annihilated in arbitrary numbers. The law of baryon conservation has been tested experimentally to phenomenally high precision (so that there is no chance that our world will collapse from the instability of protons within the next few hundred billion years) and the two lepton-conservation laws are also reasonably certain. Nevertheless, we have no theoretical understanding of the basis of these laws.

Is the exploring physicist nearing the end in the discovery of new particles? It would be very rash to say so. In the period 1960–1964 the muon's neutrino has been identified, a number of the new short-lived resonances have been found, and the omega particle has been discovered. The list of "elementary" objects will probably increase before it decreases again, and will include a spectrum of particles whose lifetimes vary from the incredibly short to the infinitely long.

In most of the rest of this book we shall be coming to grips with the ideas about nature which the particles have generated or have illuminated. Before doing so, it is essential to understand the meaning of various quantities such as charge, mass, and energy which characterize the behavior of the particles, and to visualize the scale of the particle world. These are the goals of Chapter Two.

Chapter Two

The Large and the Small

It is easy to talk about the "incredibly short" lifetime of an elementary particle or about the "fantastically small" size of an atomic nucleus. It is not so easy to visualize these things. On the submicroscopic frontier of science (as well as on the cosmological frontier) man has proceeded so far away from the familiar scale of the world encompassed by his senses, that he must make a real effort of the imagination to relate these new frontiers to the ordinary world. But the reward of being able to think pictorially over the whole panorama, from infinitesimal to enormous, adequately repays the effort.

In order to describe nature, the scientist needs a number of concepts which are so well defined that they are not merely descriptive ideas but are measurable quantities. The simplest of these are the ideas of size (length measurement) and duration (time measurement). Each property of an elementary particle—its mass, electric charge, energy, spin, angular momentum—is such a measurable concept. Roughly, a measurable, or quantitative, concept is anything to which both a name and a number can be attached, for example, 6 inches, 90 miles per hour, 30 minutes, 110 volts. (Soldiers, sailors, and prisoners, although they have both a name and a number, do not qualify. The number must be an indication of size or quantity, not a serial number.)

For each of the concepts used to describe nature, a unit of measurement is introduced to allow meaningful comparisons of measurements in different places or at different times. This is a long way of saying something we all know from daily life. Our height is expressed in terms of feet and inches, our weight in pounds, our age in years. Each quantity needs a unit in terms of which it can be expressed. Unfortunately there is no international agreement about units (although the situation is much less chaotic within science than in the everyday world) but this circumstance of a multiplicity of units serves all the better to demonstrate the need for units. An American, asked his weight, might answer, "I weigh 154." An Englishman of the same size weighs 11. A Frenchman of similar build might claim to weigh 70. Their weights are all the same, of course, but the American is reckoning in pounds, the Englishman in stone, and the Frenchman in kilograms. A statement of the number without the unit is quite meaningless, although in a sufficiently provincial gathering the unit may, by common agreement, be understood and therefore not stated.

There are in science some "pure" numbers, also called dimensionless numbers. These numbers in fact hold a special fascination for scientists just because they are independent of any set of units. If we say, "Table 1 lists twelve kinds of particles," the "twelve" is a pure number, the result of counting, and refers to no particular unit. But in the main the quantities needed to describe the particles do require units.

The normal scientific units, such as the centimeter of length (frequently abbreviated cm) and the second of time, are "man-sized" units adopted for convenience in our macroscopic world. The centimeter, about half an inch, is roughly the thickness of a man's finger; in one second a man can blink a few times, say "one thousand and one," or stroll about a hundred centimeters. These units are handy and easy to visualize. But in the worlds of the large and the small they become ridiculously inappropriate. The distance from earth to sun is an enormous number of centimeters; the size of a hydrogen atom, a tiny fraction of one centimeter. The age of the earth is a vast number of seconds, the lifetime of a pion an imperceptible part of a second. Journalists are fond of writing out numbers from the cosmological or submicroscopic world in their full glory, with a string of zeros before or after the decimal point: The pion lives 0.000000026 second; the number of hydrogen atoms in a quart of water is 60,000,000,000,000,000,000,000,000. These numbers are impressive, but a bit confusing and not very instructive.

Scientists have done two things about this situation. First, and most simply, they have replaced the lengthy newspaper notation for large and small numbers by what is called the exponential notation. In this notation one hundred is written 10^2, one thousand is 10^3, one million is 10^6, three million is 3×10^6, forty billion dollars (the U. S. defense budget) is 4×10^{10} dollars. The long number in the preceding paragraph is 6×10^{25}. The exponent, or power of ten, may be looked upon as an instruction to shift the decimal point so many places to the right. Two million is 2×10^6, that is, two followed by six zeros, 2,000,000. This notation is so simple and convenient that everyone should know it.

Multiplication is carried out by *adding* exponents. One billion is one thousand millions: 10^6 multiplied by 10^3 is 10^9. If the average American has savings of \$200 (2×10^2), and there are 180 million average Americans (180×10^6, or 1.8×10^8), then the total savings are \$$2 \times 10^2$ multiplied by 1.8×10^8, which is \$$3.6 \times 10^{10}$, or 36 billion dollars. If light travels at 3×10^{10} cm per second, and there are 3×10^7 seconds in one year, then one light-year, the distance traveled by light in one year, is 3×10^{10} multiplied by 3×10^7, that is, 9×10^{17} cm. This is a large number; it is about 300 million times around the earth. Returning to dollars, if 9×10^{17} dollars were divided equally among the world's population, every man, woman, and child would control a fortune of nearly half a billion dollars.

The exponential notation is also used for small numbers. One tenth is 10^{-1}; one millionth is 10^{-6}; three billionths is 3×10^{-9}. The rule for adding exponents still holds in multiplication. For example, $10^{-3} \times 10^9$ equals 10^6, recalling that adding a negative number is the same as subtracting a positive number. In words, one thousandth of one billion is one million. The lifetime of a muon is 2×10^{-6} seconds, that is, two millionths of a second. The size of an atom is about 10^{-8} cm, or one one-hundred millionth of a centimeter.

The second approach to dealing with large and small quantities is to invent new units more appropriate to the domain being considered. Thus, for cosmological purposes, the light-year (which we calculated above to be 9×10^{17} cm) is a convenient unit of length. For dealing with atoms, the Angstrom unit, equal to 10^{-8} cm, is frequently used; for nuclear and particle phenomena the fermi (10^{-13} cm), one hundred thousand times smaller, is a more suitable unit. In Table 1 we followed this approach, adopting the spin of the photon as the unit spin, the charge of the proton as the unit charge, and the mass of the electron as the unit mass. It is, of course, still necessary to know how to convert these units back to the conventional units, just as it is necessary to know how to convert among centimeters, inches, feet, yards, miles, and light-years.

Table 2 summarizes some of the quantities used to characterize the world of elementary particles.

TABLE 2. TABLE OF MEASUREMENTS

Physical quantity	Common unit in the large-scale world	Scale of the submicroscopic world
Length	Centimeter (about half an inch)	Size of atom about 10^{-8} cm = 1 Angstrom unit Size of particle about 10^{-13} cm = 1 fermi
Speed	Centimeter per second (speed of a snail)	Speed of light = 3×10^{10} cm/sec
Time	Second (the swing of a pendulum)	Natural time unit of particle about 10^{-23} sec Typical lifetime of a "long-lived" particle about 10^{-10} sec
Mass	Gram (mass of one cubic centimeter of water)	Mass of electron = 9×10^{-28} gm
Energy	Erg (energy of a lazy bug) Food calorie (40 billion ergs)	1 ev (electron volt) = 1.6×10^{-12} erg Air molecule has about one fortieth ev Proton in largest accelerator about 30 billion ev
Charge	Coulomb (lights a lamp for one second)	Electron charge = 1.6×10^{-19} coulomb
Spin	Gm $\times$ cm $\times$ cm/sec (grasshopper turning around)	Spin of photon = $\hbar$ = 10^{-27} gm $\times$ cm $\times$ cm/sec

Length

One of the best ways to try to visualize the very great or the very small is by analogy. For example, to picture the nucleus, whose size is about 10^{-4} to 10^{-5} of the size of an atom, one may imagine the atom expanded to, say, 10,000 feet (10^4 feet) or nearly two miles. This is about the length of a runway at a large air terminal such as New York International Airport. A fraction 10^{-4} of this is one foot, or about the diameter of a basketball. A fraction 10^{-5} is ten times smaller, or about the diameter of a golf ball. A golf ball in the middle of New York International Airport is about as lonely as the proton at the center of a hydrogen atom. The basketball would correspond to a heavy nucleus such as uranium. On this scale, one centimeter would be expanded to 2×10^8 (200 million) miles, or about twice the distance from earth to sun. To arrive at the number of atoms in a cubic centimeter of water (a few drops), first cover the earth with airports, one against the other. Then go up a mile or so and build another solid layer of airports. Do this 100 million times. The last layer will have reached out to the sun and will contain some 10^{16} airports (ten million billion). The number of atoms in a few drops of water will be the number of airports filling up this substantial part of the solar system. If the airport-construction rate were *one million* each second, the job could just have been finished in the known lifetime of the universe (something over 10 billion years).

The size of a proton is about 10^{-13} cm; this distance has been given the name fermi, in honor of Enrico Fermi, who pioneered studies of the nuclear particles in the 1930's. The smallest distance probed in any experiment so far conducted is about a tenth of a fermi, or 10^{-14} cm. Most of the elementary particles have a size of about 1 fermi, but a few, such as the electron, may be much smaller.

Although the cosmological world is outside the scope of this book, it is of some interest to compare the astronomical scale of size with the submicroscopic. The known part of the universe extends out to about 10^{10} light-years, or 10^{28} cm. Man, a creature about 10^2 cm high, is thus smaller than the universe by a factor of 10^{26}, but larger than a proton by a factor of "only" 10^{15}. The universe is about as much larger than the whole solar system as man is larger than the proton. From the smallest known distance (10^{-14} cm) to the largest (10^{28} cm), man has spanned a factor of 10^{42} in size. The number 10^{42} is so enormous that not even analogy is of much help in comprehending it. Suppose we wanted to let the population explosion run its course until there were 10^{42} people. The earth itself can only accommodate a bit over 10^{15} people standing shoulder to shoulder. A million earths similarly packed could handle 10^{21}. To reach our goal of 10^{42} people, we would have to make each couple on these million earths personally responsible for finding and peopling to the limit a million new earths. This would require 10^{27} earths altogether, a substantial number. There are only about 10^{23} stars in the universe. If every star had ten planets, and every planet was packed with people like sardines in a can, the universe would still not hold as many as 10^{42} people.

Thinking up ways to picture large and small numbers can be a fascinating game. It is recommended that the reader try it himself.

Speed

A snail in a hurry can travel at a speed of about 1 centimeter per second (or, in briefer scientific notation, 1 cm/sec). A man strolls at about 10^2 cm/sec, drives a car at 3×10^3 cm/sec, and rides in a jet plane at near the speed of sound, which is 3×10^4 cm/sec (about 700 miles per hour).

In distance, man has encountered no limit, large or small. But, in speed, nature seems to have established a very definite limit, the speed of light, 3×10^{10} cm/sec. This is exactly a million times the speed of sound in air, an easy ratio to remember. Even an astronaut falls short of the speed of light by a factor of forty thousand. He needs an hour and a half to get once around the earth, while a photon (if it could be caused to travel in a curved path) could complete the trip in a tenth of a second. Still, man is not so far removed from nature's top speed as he is from the frontiers in space and time.

Atoms and molecules, executing their continual restless motion in solids, liquids, and gases on earth, move sluggishly about at only one to ten times the speed of sound in air, a factor 10^5 to 10^6 short of the speed of light. But for elementary particles, speeds near the speed of light are common. The photon and neutrinos have no choice, of course, and travel at exactly the speed of light (as does the graviton). In all of the larger modern accelerators, particles with mass—usually electrons or protons—are pushed very near to the speed of light, and the unstable particles formed in nuclear collisions also frequently emerge with speeds near the speed of light.

Astronauts in science fiction frequently shift into "superdrive" and scoot about the galaxy above the speed of light. Is there any chance that this will become reality? It is extremely unlikely, and for a very simple reason. The lighter an object is, the more easily it can be accelerated. Freight trains lumber slowly up to speed, automobiles more quickly, and protons in a cyclotron still more quickly. A particle with no mass whatever should be the easiest to accelerate; indeed, the massless photon jumps instantaneously to the speed of light when it is created. But not beyond. If anything at all were able to go faster than light, then light itself, being composed of massless photons, should go faster.

Time

In dealing with the time scale of elementary particles, it is essential first to get rid of preconceived notions about what is a "short" time or a "long" time. A millionth of a second certainly seems to qualify as a short time, yet for an elementary particle it is an exceedingly long time. On the other hand, a million years is the mere blink of an eye for the stately cosmological march of events.

If an automobile had its last bolt tightened at the end of the assembly line, then was driven a hundred feet away, where it promptly collapsed in a heap, we should say that it had had a short lifetime. If it covered some 20 billion miles before collapsing, we should say that it had had an amazingly long lifetime, indeed, that it was the most extraordinarily long-lived car ever built. Let us translate these distances to the elementary-particle world. The size of a particle is about 10^{-13} cm; it travels typically at about 10^{10} cm/sec. Thus, to cover a distance ten times its own size (comparable to the car moving 100 feet), the particle needs only 10^{-22} sec. The duration, 10^{-23} sec, is a kind of natural time unit for a particle. Yet almost every particle in Table 1 lives at least 10^{-10} sec, an enormously long time compared to 10^{-23} sec. In 10^{-10} sec the particle can cover a whole centimeter, more than a million million times its own size. A particle moving one centimeter is comparable to a car going 20 billion miles. Any particle that can move one centimeter away from its birthplace before dying deserves to be called long-lived. The pion and muon, with lifetimes of 10^{-8} sec and 10^{-6} sec, respectively, can move much farther even than 1 cm. The neutron is a strange special case. Its lifetime of 17 minutes is practically infinite for the elementary-particle world.

The new particles, or "resonances," now being discovered have lifetimes of 10^{-20} sec or less. They are indeed short lived and perhaps they do not even deserve to be called particles. They are like the car which collapses before it gets out of the factory gate. The manufacturer might be tempted to say, "That was no car; it was just an unstable phenomenon with a transitory existence" (for which the physicist uses the word "resonance").

Since the shortest distance probed experimentally is about 10^{-14} cm, it is fair to say that the shortest known time interval is 10^{-24} sec (although direct time measurements are still very far from reaching this short an interval). The longest known time is the "lifetime of the universe," that is, the apparent duration of the expansion of the universe, which is also a few times the age of the earth. This amounts to about 10^{18} sec (30 billion years). The ratio of these is 10^{42}, the same enormous number as the ratio of the largest and smallest distances. This is not a coincidence. The outermost reaches of the universe are moving away from us at a speed near the speed of light and the particles used to probe the submicroscopic world are moving at speeds near the speed of light. On both the cosmological and submicroscopic frontiers, the speed of light appears to be the natural link between distance and time measurements.

Mass

The technical definition of mass is rather complicated and we have no need to go into it in detail. It will be adequate for our present purposes to think of the mass of an object as the amount of material in the object. This is actually a very unscientific definition, but it provides a way of thinking about mass. The idea of mass is confused by the circumstance that the pull of gravity on an object is proportional to the mass in the object. A parcel of large mass on a postal scale is pulled down more strongly than a parcel of small mass and consequently causes the scale to show a higher reading. We say that the more massive object "weighs" more; that is, it is pulled more strongly by the earth, and in fact in exact proportion to its mass.

To understand mass a bit better, imagine some astronauts floating freely inside the cabin of their space ship in a weightless condition. If two of them join hands, then push and let go, they will float apart—in a particular way. The larger man will move away a bit more slowly than the smaller man; we attribute this to his greater mass. The important fact about mass is that it is a measure of resistance to a change of motion, a property usually called inertia. If a single astronaut floating in mid cabin tosses a baseball, he will recoil and drift backward slowly as the ball moves swiftly off in the opposite direction. If the ball leaves the point of separation five hundred times faster than the astronaut, it is because its mass is only one five-hundredth as great as the astronaut's, and it has, therefore, five hundred times less resistance to being set into motion. Anyone who has fired a gun knows about recoil. If a hunter had no more mass than his bullet, he and the bullet would be accelerated to equal speed. Because he has a great deal more mass—hence, more inertia—than the bullet, he has more resistance to being set into motion and is moved much more slowly than the bullet.

On the human scale, the elementary particles have exceedingly small masses. It is therefore relatively easy to set them into high-speed motion and they normally fly about near the speed of light. The massless particles have, in fact, no resistance whatever to being speeded up, and upon being created, move instantly at the speed of light.

The electron is the lightest particle with nonvanishing mass and it is therefore usual to adopt the mass of the electron as a convenient unit in the submicroscopic world, as we did in Table 1. The heaviest particle, the omega, is more than 3,000 times heavier than the electron, yet a million million omegas would not be able to tip the world's most sensitive balance.

The scientific unit of mass is the gram, about the mass of an average vitamin pill. A quart of water has a mass of about 900 grams. The transatlantic air traveler is permitted a mass of luggage of 20,000 grams (tourist class), or 20 kilograms, which is about 44 pounds. The electron's mass is 9×10^{-28} gm, that of the "heavy" omega particle about 3×10^{-24} gm.

To end the discussion of mass on a cosmic note we ask, what is the mass of the universe? This is certainly not well known, but a rough estimate can be made. There are about 10^{23} stars in the universe (this number is roughly the same as the number of molecules in a gram of water). An average star weighs about 10^{35} gm, making the total mass some 10^{58} gm. Each gram of matter contains about 10^{24} protons, so that what we know of the universe contains (very roughly) 10^{82} protons.*

Energy

The most remarkable fact about energy is its diversity. Like a clever actor who can assume many guises, energy appears in a variety of forms, and can shift from one role to another. Because of this richness of form, energy appears in nearly every part of the description of nature and can make a good claim to be the most important single concept in science.

One common form of energy is energy of motion, kinetic energy, which is a measure of how much force over how great a distance is required to set an object into motion or to bring it to rest. The faster a particle moves, the more kinetic energy it possesses. This is not far removed from our everyday use of the word; for example, in speaking of a "energetic" person, we refer to someone in constant motion, capable of doing a great deal of work. Work itself has a technical definition in physics, force multiplied by distance; and energy is the capacity for doing work. Every form of energy, if suitably transformed, can do work. Heat energy, for example, is the accumulated kinetic energy of the restless random motion of molecules, and a steam engine is a device which derives mechanical work from heat energy.

The great significance of energy springs in part from the variety of its manifestations, in part from the fact that it is conserved—that the total amount of energy remains always the same, with the loss of one kind of energy being compensated by the gain of another kind of energy. Trace, for example, the flow of energy from sun to earth to man; this illustrates both the variety and the conservation of energy. When protons in the sun unite to form helium nuclei, nuclear energy is released. This energy may go first to the kinetic energy of motion of nuclei, which contributes to the sun's heat energy. Some of the energy is then carried away from the sun by photons, the particles which are bundles of electromagnetic energy. The energy content of the photons may be transformed,

---

* The known part of the universe presumably contains a like number of electrons, about 10^{82}. It contains fewer neutrinos, perhaps about 10^{79}, but uncountably many photons and gravitons. The unstable particles, on the other hand, are far less numerous than protons.

by the complicated and not yet fully understood process of photo-synthesis, into stored chemical energy in plants. Either by eating plants or by eating animals which ate plants, man acquires this solar energy, which is then made available to power his brain and muscles and to keep him warm.

That mass is one of the forms of energy was first realized at the beginning of this century. The energy of mass and the energy of motion are the two forms of energy which dominate the ele-mentary-particle world. Mass energy can be thought of as the "energy of being," matter possessing energy just by virtue of exist-ing. A material particle is nothing more than a highly concentrated and localized bundle of energy. The amount of concentrated energy for a motionless particle is proportional to its mass. If the particle is moving it has still more energy, its kinetic energy. A massless particle such as a photon has only energy of motion (kinetic energy) and no energy of being (mass).

Einstein's most famous equation,

$$E = mc^2,$$

provides the relation between the mass, m, of a particle and its intrinsic energy, or energy of being, E. The quantity c in this formula is the speed of light; c^2 is the notation for $c \times c$, the square of the speed of light. The important statement Einstein's equation makes is that energy is proportional to mass. Twice as much mass means twice as much intrinsic energy; no mass means no intrinsic energy. The factor c^2 is called a constant of proportionality and does the job of converting from the units in which mass is expressed to the units in which energy is expressed. By analogy, consider the equation giving the cost of filling your car with gasoline,

$$C = GP.$$

The cost, C, is equal to the number of gallons, G, multiplied by the price per gallon, P. The cost is proportional to the number of gallons and P is the constant of proportionality which converts the number of gallons to a total cost. In a similar way, c^2 is a price. It is energy per unit mass, the price which must be paid in energy to create a unit of mass.

In an isolated nuclear collision, or particle reaction, the total energy remains unchanged. In fact, practically every event in the submicroscopic world *is* isolated, for the distance over which the particles interact with one another is generally exceedingly small compared with the distance between neighboring atoms, about 10^{-8} cm. The individual event occurs with the particles effectively unaware of anything else in the universe. In a collision, or a reaction, or a decay process, there are two ways in which energy may be supplied. A particle may be slowed down, thus giving up some of its kinetic energy; or a particle with mass may be destroyed, thus giving up its intrinsic energy. Analogously, energy may be taken up in two ways. A particle may be speeded up or a new particle may be created. The rule of energy conservation can be stated as follows: The total energy supplied must be equal to the total energy taken up; that is, the energy loss must equal the energy gain.

Consider, for example, the decay of a pion at rest. Since it is motionless its only energy is the intrinsic energy associated with its mass. It decays spontaneously into a muon and a neutrino. The vanishing of the pion makes its mass energy available. Some of this is used to create the mass of the lighter muon. The rest is supplied as energy of motion, and the muon and neutrino fly off at high speed with just enough kinetic energy to make up the difference. This example makes clear why a particle can decay spontaneously only into other particles lighter than itself. In a high-energy collision, on the other hand, such as those which occur near a particle accelerator, the projectile particle may be slowed down and some of its kinetic energy made available to create the mass of new particles. This is the way in which antiprotons and the various unstable particles are created in the modern high-energy laboratory.

The average citizen who pays an electric bill and watches his weight is probably aware of at least two of the energy units in common use, the kilowatt-hour and the food calorie. Ten 100-watt light bulbs require a kilowatt; if they all remain lit for one hour, one kilowatt-hour of energy is used up. Reasonably enough, it is electrical energy for which one pays. An overweight person might remark that it is also calories for which one pays. One food calorie is the energy released by a good-sized pinch of sugar when it is oxidized. A thousand or more calories of energy are needed each day to keep the human machine running efficiently.

A more usual scientific unit of energy is called the erg. It is actually quite small, being the energy of motion of a 2-gram bug crawling at 1 cm/sec. A food calorie, for example, is some 40 billion (4×10^{10}) ergs, and a kilowatt-hour is nearly a thousand times larger still, being 3.6×10^{13} ergs. Nevertheless, the erg is considerably larger than the energies usually encountered in the submicroscopic world, where another energy unit, the electron volt, has been introduced (the last energy unit we shall mention!). The electron volt is about one millionth of one millionth of an erg (1.6×10^{-12} erg, to be exact).*

The average kinetic energy of the incessant random motion of molecules and atoms provides a kind of a baseline for energy comparisons in the world of the very small. A single molecule at normal temperatures moves about with an average kinetic energy of about one fortieth of an electron volt. On the much hotter surface of the sun this thermal motion averages about half an electron volt. But in accelerators man can readily push the energies of particles to much higher values. Early cyclotrons accelerated protons to over one million electron volts (1 Mev). Other accelerators completed after World War II pushed the energy of protons toward one billion electron volts (1 Bev). The Bevatron in Berkeley (whose name obviously has something to do with its energy) accelerates protons to 6 Bev. The largest accelerators operational in 1964 are in Brookhaven, New York, and Geneva, Switzerland; as projectiles, both use protons that reach an energy of over 30 Bev. Some of the cosmic-ray particles from outer space arrive with energies even much greater than this. How these particles are accelerated to such enormous energies remains a mystery.

Since mass and energy are equivalent, how much energy is needed to create the mass of an elementary particle? The creation of the lightest particle, the electron, requires 500,000 electron volts. The older accelerators were capable of supplying sufficient energy to create positrons and electrons. But the proton mass is equivalent to nearly 1 billion electron volts. The production of antiprotons had to await the construction of the 6 Bev Bevatron. The new 30 Bev machines can create all of the known particles with energy to spare; it is quite possible that new and still heavier particles may be discovered with the help of these accelerators.

Mass is a very potent and highly concentrated form of energy. The power of the atomic bomb, in which less than a tenth of one per cent of the mass is converted to energy, serves as an eloquent

---

* The electron volt has nothing special to do with the electron. It is the energy given to *any* charged elementary particle (since all carry the same size of charge) by an electrical potential of one volt.

reminder of this fact. To understand this in terms of the energy equivalents given above, recall the typical energies of thermal motion. Even on the white-hot surface of the sun, a proton has a kinetic energy of less than 1 ev, a mere nothing compared with the billion ev locked up in its mass. The mass of a single proton converted to energy on the earth is sufficient to heat up a billion atoms to a temperature higher than that of the sun's surface.

Charge

Electric charge is best described as being like French perfume. It is that certain something worn by particles which makes them attractive—specifically, attractive to the opposite kind of particle. Particles that do not have it are called neutral and have no influence (at least no electrical influence) on other particles. Charge can lead to pairing of particles; the hydrogen atom, for example, consists of a proton and electron held together by electrical attraction. More energetic particles are not held together by the electric force; it merely causes them to deviate slightly from a straight course.

The charge carried by a particle may be positive or negative. Two charges of the same kind repel each other, two of opposite kinds attract. The protons within a nucleus, for example, repel each other, but the overpowering nuclear force nevertheless holds the nucleus together. Eventually, however, for very heavy nuclei, the electrical repulsion becomes more than the nuclear forces can counteract, and the nucleus flies apart. It is for this reason that no nuclei heavier than uranium exist in nature.

Which charge is called positive and which negative is entirely arbitrary, and is the result of historical accident. The definition that led to electrons being negative and protons positive probably stems from a guess made by Benjamin Franklin about the middle of the eighteenth century. His choice of nomenclature was based on the erroneous supposition that it is positive electricity which flows most readily from one object to another. We now know that it is the negative electrons which are mobile and account for the flow of electric current in metals.

Charge is still very mysterious to the physicist. He understands it little better than he understands the workings of French perfume. If we think of a particle as a small structure spread out over a tiny region of space, it is logical to think of its charge as being spread out too. But if this is so, why do the various bits of charge making up the particle not repel each other and cause the whole particle to disintegrate and fly apart? No one knows a satisfactory answer to this question. It is also perplexing that all particles have exactly the same magnitude of charge. If the charge of the electron is called $-e$ (it is negative) then the charge of every other particle is either $-e$ or $+e$ or zero. No other possibilities are realized in nature. We have no understanding of this fact, and also have no clue as to why the electron has the charge it does have, rather than some other value. The true nature of charge and the reason it comes only in lumps of a certain size are among the most important problems in elementary-particle physics.

The fact that we do not understand charge at a fundamental level has been no hindrance to making extensive use of charge for practical purposes. Electrons can be detached from atoms rather readily—at least in certain metals called conductors—and by means of electrical forces they can be pushed and pulled through wires or sent flying through empty space, as within a vacuum tube or a television tube. Almost all of the fine control and all of the communications in the world are effected by electrons in electronic circuits. A great part of the world's heavy labor is also done by electrons turning motors or supplying heat.

The fact that there is a voltage across the two holes in a household electrical outlet means that an electric force is standing ready to do some work. If an electric light is plugged in, the electrons are sent flying from one prong of the plug, through the light (where they expend some energy which appears as light and heat), then back to the other prong. The number of electrons involved in such a flow is enormous. In a typical household light bulb, about 10^{19} electrons flow through the filament each second. In heavy machinery or in the high-tension lines connecting cities, the number is far greater. Even through the tiniest and most delicate electronic circuit, many billions of electrons flow each second.

If a comb is passed through dry hair, perhaps a million million electrons leave the hair and stick on the comb. Nevertheless, the comb is almost neutral. For every extra electron it has acquired the comb has a million million neutral atoms. It is fortunate for us that the objects in our macroscopic world remain always almost neutral. If the comb acquired anything close to an electrification of one extra electron per atom, the consequence would be dire. Either there would be a powerful and deadly bolt of lightning from comb to man as the charge was neutralized or the enormous force of electrical attraction would draw the comb back so violently that it would be a dangerous weapon.

Intrinsically, the electrical force in nature is a great deal stronger than the gravitational force and in the submicroscopic world the gravitational force is usually ignored altogether. The matter in our macroscopic world, however, exists in such a fine state of electrical balance that gravity has a chance to make itself felt. In every object in our world, the number of positive charges is almost precisely equal to the number of negative charges. The effects nearly cancel, and what we regard as marked electrical effects arise from an exceedingly tiny imbalance in positive and negative charge. If a big imbalance were ever realized (there is no chance of this) the disastrous result would make the force of gravity appear to be truly inconsequential.

One of the common scientific units of charge is the coulomb, named for the French scientist, Charles A. Coulomb, who discovered the exact law of electrical force in 1785. One coulomb is roughly the amount of charge that moves through a 100-watt light bulb in a second, or through an electric iron in a fifth of a second. (The coulomb is not commonly encountered in the house, but a very closely related unit, the ampere, is. On a household fuse one might see stamped "15 amp." The ampere, or amp for short, is one coulomb per second. If more than 15 coulombs of charge flow through this fuse each second, a wire inside it will melt and stop the flow.) The basic unit of charge in the world of particles is the electron charge, 1.6×10^{-19} coulombs. This is less than one billionth of one billionth of one coulomb.

Spin

Rotational motion seems to be a characteristic of most of the structures in the universe, from neutrinos to galaxies. Our earth rotates on its axis once a day, and rotates once around the sun in a year. The sun itself turns on its axis once in 26 days and, along with the other stars of our galaxy, travels once around the galaxy in 230 million years. It is not known whether larger structures, such as clusters of galaxies, have an over-all rotational motion, but it would be surprising if they do not.

Going down the scale, the atoms that compose molecules can rotate about each other, and do, although at a rate which varies from time to time as the molecule is disturbed by its neighbors.

Within the atom, electrons rotate about the nucleus at speeds of from one per cent up to more than ten per cent of the speed of light, thereby giving a kind of solidity to the sphere of empty space in which they move. The remarkable fact that the electron also spins like a top about its own axis was first discovered in 1925 and now we know that many particles have this property of intrinsic spin.

The spin of an elementary particle unlike, say, the rotation of a molecule, is an invariable property of that particle, always fixed at a definite value. The electron can not be stopped from rotating, nor can its rotation be speeded up. The spin of an electron is such an essential feature of the electron that it can be changed only at the expense of destroying the electron altogether. Actually, this is a rather subtle point. It is probably more accurate to say that if the electron is caused to spin more rapidly, this so drastically changes the properties of the electron that it is more convenient to think of the resulting structure as a completely new and distinct particle. To what extent the different particles are really independent and to what extent they are only different states of motion of some common underlying structure is, of course, the great, unsolved problem of particle physics, and it would be idle to speculate further about this point here. It can only be re-emphasized that physicists retain their faith that there exists a simpler structure underlying the particles.

Spin is measured in terms of the quantity called angular momentum (discussed in Chapter One), which is a combined measure of the mass, the size, and the speed of the rotating system. The rate of rotation of an electron can not actually be measured but it has to be so great that the charge within the electron is moving at nearly the speed of light. In spite of this frantic rate of rotation, the electron is not able to generate much angular momentum because of its small size and small mass. A man swiveling slowly in his chair to watch a tennis match has at least 10^{33} times more angular momentum than a single electron.

As the electron carries nature's smallest unit of electric charge, it also carries the indivisible unit of spin, which, for historical reasons, is denoted by $\frac{1}{2}\hbar$. At the turn of this century, Max Planck discovered the existence of a constant in nature which relates the frequency and the energy of photons (this relation will be discussed in Chapter Five). We now call it Planck's constant and write it h. About ten years later Niels Bohr discovered that this constant also has something to do with the rotation of electrons about the nucleus in an atom. In their orbits about the nucleus the electrons have an angular momentum which is always equal to h divided by 2π ($h/2\pi$) or two times $h/2\pi$ or three times $h/2\pi$, and so on, never any value between. Since it is a nuisance to write out the extra factor of 2π whenever it occurs, the notation $\hbar$ (pronounced "h bar") has come into common use for $h/2\pi$. Finally, when Samuel Goudsmit and George Uhlenbeck discovered in 1925 that the electron spins, they found that its spin angular momentum is not $\hbar$, which had been thought to be the indivisible unit, but only $\frac{1}{2}\hbar$. The quantity $\hbar$ has been adopted as the unit of spin and angular momentum in the submicroscopic world, even though the smallest indivisible unit is only half so great. The leptons and baryons all have spin $\frac{1}{2}$, the photon has spin 1, and the graviton spin 2, in this unit.

For the record, $\hbar$ is equal to 1.0544×10^{-27} gm $\times$ cm $\times$ cm/sec (the units are mass $\times$ size $\times$ speed). Recall that π is the number $3.14159 \cdot \cdot \cdot$, which occurs in geometry as the ratio of the circumference of a circle to its diameter.

The principle of spin quantization applies in the macroscopic world as well as in the microscopic, but is too subtle an effect ever to be measured for a large object. When the spectator at a tennis tournament turns to follow the ball, his angular momentum, in units of $\hbar$, might be 10^{33} or $10^{33} + 1$ or $10^{33} + 2$, but never $10^{33} + \frac{1}{3}$. The increment $\hbar$ between allowed values is so infinitesimal that it is entirely beyond hope ever to notice this discreteness in the macroscopic world. A change of one penny in the gross national product of the United States is a disturbance more than a billion billion times greater than a change by one unit of the spectator's angular momentum. It is no wonder that man did not discover the quantum theory of angular momentum until he was able to study in detail the structure of a system as small as an atom.

The units of measurement man normally uses, even in scientific work, have been defined in an arbitrary way, chosen merely for convenience. They have nothing to do with "natural units" and are not in particular harmony with the basic structure of the world. Yet in this century we have learned of the existence of two natural units which are now commonly employed in studying the elementary particles. It seems quite likely that a deeper understanding of the particles will be accompanied by the discovery of a third natural unit.

The meter was originally defined as one ten-millionth of the distance from the earth's pole to the equator. (It is not quite that, since the meter was standardized in the nineteenth century, but the knowledge of the size of the earth has been improved since then.) The centimeter, in turn, is one one-hundredth of a meter. The gram is then defined as the mass of a cube of water one centimeter on a side. Both the centimeter and the gram thus depend on the size of the earth, and there is no reason to believe that there is anything very special about the size of the earth. The third basic unit, the second, also depends on a property of our earth, its rate of rotation—again, nothing very special. For no better reasons than that the Egyptians divided the day and the night into twelfths and the Sumerians liked to count in sixties, the hour is one twenty-fourth of a day, the minute a sixtieth of an hour, and the second a sixtieth of a minute.

Within the first five years of this century two natural units were discovered which appeared to be obvious choices for a basis of measurement in the submicroscopic world. These were the speed of light c and Planck's constant h. Neither is directly a mass, a length, or a time, but they are simple combinations of these three. If they were joined by a third natural unit, they would form a basis of measurement as complete as, and much more satisfying than, the gram, the centimeter, and the second. (The thoughtful reader might propose the charge on the electron as an obvious candidate for the third natural unit. Unfortunately, it will not serve, for it is not independent of c and h—just as speed is not independent of time and distance.)

The fact that light travels at a fixed speed c has been known for several centuries, but the central significance of this speed in nature could be appreciated only when the theory of relativity was developed. Relativity revealed first of all that c is a natural speed limit, attainable not only by light but by any massless particle. The theory also showed that this constant appeared in various surprising places which had nothing to do with speed, for instance, in the mass-energy relation, $E = mc^2$. Planck's constant was brand new in 1900, but its significance also mounted over the next few decades as it came to be recognized as the fundamental constant of the quantum theory, governing not only the allowed values of spin, but every other quantized quantity.

It has to be recognized that every measurement is really the statement of a ratio. If you say you weigh 151 pounds you are, in effect, saying your weight is 151 times greater than the weight of a standard object (a pint of water), which is arbitrarily called one pound. A 50-minute class is 50 times longer than the arbitrarily defined time unit, the minute. When one uses natural units, the ratio is taken with respect to some physically significant unit rather than an arbitrary one. On the natural scale, a jet-plane speed of $10^{-6}c$ is very slow, a particle speed of $0.99c$ is very fast. An angular momentum of $10,000\hbar$ is large, an angular momentum of $\frac{1}{2}\hbar$ is small.

The difficult point to recognize here is that once the speed of light has been adopted as the unit of speed, it no longer makes any sense to ask how fast light travels. The only answer is: Light goes as fast as it goes. Since every measurement is really a comparison, there must always be at least one standard that can not be compared with anything but itself. This leads to the idea of a "dimensionless physics." Having agreed on a standard of speed, we can say a jet plane travels at a speed of 10^{-6}, that is, at one one-millionth of the speed of light. The 10^{-6} is a pure number to which no unit need be attached; it is the ratio of the speed of the plane to the speed of light. To make possible a dimensionless physics we need one more independent natural unit, and this has not yet emerged. This unit, if it is found, may be a length, and there is much speculation that such a unit will be connected with a whole new view of the nature of space (and of time) in the world of the very small.

It should be added that a dimensionless physics is not so profound as it may sound, nor would it necessarily be a terminus of man's downward probing. Its lack of profundity springs from the fact that it, too, would rest on an arbitrary agreement among men about units. The hope is, however, that all scientists will be led naturally and uniquely to agree that there is only one sensible set of natural units, in contrast with the present situation, where the fact about which we all agree is that there is nothing special whatever about the centimeter, the gram, and the second. Even if the dimensionless physics is realized, there will remain dimensionless, or pure, numbers still to be explained, and that explanation may lie in still deeper layers of the substructure of nature.

Chapter Three

The Great Ideas of Twentieth-Century Physics

Most of the advances in our understanding of nature in this century have been made possible by two general theories—the theory of relativity and the theory of quantum mechanics. Accompanying these theories have been a number of new ideas which are completely contrary to those of "classical" science (that is, science developed before the twentieth century) and to everyday experience. Man has been forced to look at nature in a new way, and to recognize that the "common sense" distilled from his sense experiences may have little to do with the deeper sense of nature's design.

Before grappling with some of the ideas generated by these theories, it is important to appreciate just what is meant by a "theory" in physical science. It is *not* an unproved assertion or tentative explanation such as might be meant in the remark, "Oh, that's just a theory." In fact, a general theory such as quantum mechanics is very nearly the opposite. It is an exact mathematical description—or "explanation"—of the phenomena in some domain of nature, and one which is entirely successful within that domain. The theory of electromagnetism, to choose an example from classical physics, *describes and predicts* all large-scale electric and magnetic phenomena; it has been accurately tested in countless experiments. It is "true" in the sense that its predictions are in perfect accord with experience. Nevertheless, this or any other general theory may eventually be abandoned, for any of several reasons. An exception could be found to show that the scope of the theory was more limited than had been believed. A deeper theory could be found which incorporated and extended the old theory. An alternative theory, which seemed simpler or more esthetically pleasing, might be found (an unlikely prospect). Strictly speaking, even the most entrenched theory in science is a tentative explanation, but the general theories of physics are so richly supported by experimental evidence that their broad validity can not be doubted.

Quantum mechanics, the most recently discovered general theory, provides an explanation of events in the world of the very small—the motion of particles, the forces between particles, the processes of creation and annihilation of particles. The content of relativity is less easy to state in a few words. On the one hand, it is a theory of theories, imposing on all other theories the requirement that they should appear the same to observers in different states of motion. On the other hand—and this aspect is the important one for our discussion of particles—relativity is a theory of high-speed motion, whether of material particles (electrons, for example) or of nonmaterial ones (photons, for example). Because particles are both very small and very fast, they are governed by the theories of quantum mechanics and of relativity, and serve admirably to illustrate the revolutionary ideas of twentieth-century science that these theories have introduced.

A general theory such as quantum mechanics finds its most elegant expression in the language of mathematics. But to make it meaningful as a part of science, the mathematics requires interpretation: What do the symbols mean? How can they be related to observations of natural phenomena? In addition, inextricably interwoven with the theory are certain ideas and ways of thinking and ways of looking at the world around us which play a fascinating yet shadowy role in science. On the one hand, from a strictly formal point of view, these ideas are irrelevant windowdressing which are not an essential part of the theory. On the other hand, it can be argued that they are the most important product of the theory. They represent the distilled wisdom about nature extracted from the complexities of mathematics and experiments.

The nonscientist should feel a bit more sympathetic to the second point of view, for how else can he gain some insight into the advances of science? To the scientist too, whether he cares to admit it or not, the ways of thought generated by the new theories are of vital importance. They provide a platform for the next leap into the unknown. The scientist working daily with the theories of relativity and quantum mechanics gains a new kind of intuition and a new kind of common sense which are very likely essential prerequisites for probing to still deeper layers of nature. The trouble is that the scientist too is a human being, living in a macroscopic world; although he has made his peace with certain of the new ideas about nature and learned to live with them, he is no better able than the next man to cast these ideas into visualizable pictorial form. It seems unlikely that man is really capable of picturing a four-dimensional world, or a wave that is a particle that is a wave, or the strange things that happen to the space and time of an object traveling near the speed of light. It remains a most interesting open question whether man's gross size and limited imagination will eventually put bounds on his ability to explore nature, or whether he will find it possible to accommodate himself to any strange ideas that new experiments and new theories seem to force upon him.

In this chapter we shall have a look at three of the "great ideas" of twentieth-century physics and discuss some examples from the world of particles which illustrate the ideas.

Probability

One of the most important insights contributed by the theory of quantum mechanics is this: The fundamental laws of nature are laws of probability, not laws of certainty. If a hydrogen atom is put into an "excited state," that is, if some energy added to it causes the electron to move about the nucleus in a more distant orbit than normal, and the atom is left to itself, it will, after a time, get rid of its excess energy by spontaneously emitting a photon of light; in this process, the electron drops back down to a smaller orbit. The length of time the atom remains in its excited state of motion before emitting the photon is entirely uncertain and can not be calculated. But the *probability* that the photon will be emitted within any particular time interval can be calculated exactly. Quantum mechanics is an unambiguous and quantitative theory in the sense that probabilities can be calculated precisely. It is indefinite and uncertain in that one can calculate only the chance that something will happen, never what will, in fact, happen for a particular atom or system. To check the calculated probability of photon emission against experiment, a single atom will never do. One must study a great many atoms and infer the probability for a single one by observing the average behavior of the whole collection. Similarly, one could never prove with a single toss of a coin that the probability of "heads" is exactly one half. Verification would require a great many tosses.

The decay of an unstable particle affords a simple and direct test of the working of probability at the fundamental level. If a great many pions are created under identical conditions at, say, the target point in a particle accelerator, those which move away at a certain speed in a certain direction may be photographed in a cloud chamber. It will be observed that some decay into muons and neutrinos after moving a very short distance; some, after moving a greater distance; a few, after moving very much farther. There will be some average distance and correspondingly some average time for the occurrence of the decay process. If this experiment is repeated time after time, each time with a very large number of pions, the *average* lifetime of the pions will be exactly the same for every group. This average is a perfectly definite quantity, a measure of the decay probability of the pion, and it can be measured to arbitrarily high precision if a large enough group of pions is used. Nevertheless, the length of time any single pion will live is indeterminate. It might die long before most of its fellow pions, or it might outlive them all.

The idea that the fundamental processes of nature are governed by laws of probability should have hit the world of science like a bombshell. Oddly enough, it did not. It seems to have infiltrated science gradually over the first quarter of this century. Only after the quantum theory had become fully developed in about 1926 did physicists and philosophers sit up and take note of the fact that a revolution had occurred in our interpretation of natural laws.*

As early as 1899, Ernest Rutherford and others studying the newly discovered phenomenon of natural radioactivity, noticed that the decay of radioactive atoms seemed to follow a law of probability. Radioactive atoms prepared in an identical way did not behave subsequently in an identical way. Exactly as with the more modern example of the pions, some lived a short time, some a longer time; only the average time for any group was constant. Moreover,

---

* The *fundamental* role of probability in nature seems to have been first clearly emphasized by Niels Bohr, Hendrik Kramers, and John Slater in 1924. Their effort to build a new quantum theory failed, but success came the following year to Werner Heisenberg, and in 1926 Max Born gave to the new theory the probability interpretation which remains as a keystone of quantum mechanics to the present day.

a single radioactive atom might undergo a transmutation process in more than one way, for example, either by emitting an alpha particle or by emitting a beta particle. Which method the atom might choose for ending its life was also unpredictable. Yet Rutherford and his fellow physicists did not shout from the housetops that the fundamental laws of nature must be laws of probability. Why was this?

The answer is very simple. They did not recognize that they were dealing with *fundamental* laws. Probability in science was, in fact, nothing new. What was new, but not yet recognized, was that for the first time probability was appearing in simple elementary phenomena in nature.

Classical physics was built solidly on the idea that nature followed exact deterministic or causal laws. If enough was known about a particle or a light wave or any system at one time, its future behavior was, in principle, exactly calculable. There was no question about where the earth or moon would be at some future date. A bridge could be built or an electromagnet designed with solid assurance that it would not collapse or fail to work because of some unpredictable fluctuation in the laws of mechanics or electromagnetism. Indeed, the exact determinism of natural laws had a powerful effect on philosophy in the nineteenth century; one popular view was that the universe could be regarded as a giant mechanism—the "world-machine"—inevitably and relentlessly unrolling history according to a predetermined plan.

Nevertheless we are all well aware of probability in everyday life and do not need to go to the elementary-particle world to find it. As life-insurance actuaries and gamblers know, life and death and roulette wheels are governed by laws of probability. This brings us to the critical point. The probability of the macroscopic world (and of classical physics) is a probability of ignorance; the probability of the microscopic world is a fundamental probability of nature. The only reason the slot in which the roulette ball stops cannot be calculated in advance of the spin is ignorance of what the physicist calls "initial conditions." If the gambler knew every mechanical detail of the wheel, the shape and size and mass of the ball, the exact law of friction in the bearings, and the precise details of the way in which the wheel was set spinning, he could, in principle, predict the result of the spin. Needless to say, this is impossible in practice, but the "in principle" is important. The difference in the quantum-mechanical law of probability is that one can *not*, in principle, as well as in fact, calculate the exact course of an atomic event, no matter how precisely the initial conditions are known. According to quantum mechanics, one can know every possible thing there is to know about a pion, and still not be able to predict when it will decay.

We can now understand why Rutherford was not unduly surprised to discover a law of probability in radioactive decay. He assumed that he was dealing with a probability of ignorance. The interior of the atom was, as far as he knew, a complicated structure, and the apparently random nature of the decay process might have been due to unknown differences in the internal state of different atoms. Yet even before quantum mechanics was developed as a fully acceptable theory (in 1925), there were hints that the probability of the atomic world might be of a more fundamental kind. Rutherford himself discovered (with Soddy, in 1902) that radioactivity represented a sudden catastrophic change in an atom, and was not the result of a gradual process of change. This, in itself, made the radioactive transmutation appear to be a rather fundamental event. Einstein's discovery in 1905 that light could be absorbed only in discrete bundles, photons, and Bohr's theory of the hydrogen atom in 1911 also contained hints of a new fundamental role of probability, but we shall not go into the details of these discoveries here.

Probability in the world of particles shows itself in two ways. First, and most directly, it manifests itself through a randomness of microscopic events. Anyone with a luminous dial wrist watch and a Geiger counter (not altogether rare these days) can perform a simple experiment to demonstrate this. The Geiger counter should be of the common type arranged to give an audible click when a high-speed particle triggers the device. The watch is held at such a distance from the counter that the individual clicks can be heard. It will be obvious to the listener that the clicks are not coming in a regular sequence like the ticks of the watch, but occur in an apparently random fashion. Indeed, a mathematical analysis would show that they are exactly random. The time at which a given click occurs is completely unrelated to the time elapsed since the previous click or to the time at which any other click occurred.

In doing an experiment like this, one feels in unusually close touch with the submicroscopic world. The single audible click means that somewhere among the countless billions of atoms on the watch face, one nucleus has suddenly spontaneously ejected a particle at high speed and transmuted itself into a different nucleus. Very literally, a nuclear explosion has occurred and, in the private world of the nucleus, the time at which the explosion occurred has been governed exclusively by a law of probability. An identical neighboring nucleus may have long since exploded, or it may be destined to live yet a long time.

Probability manifests itself in another way that is not so obvious to the eye or ear, but is equally convincing to someone with a little mathematical training. This is through the exponential law of decay. Rutherford, in fact, discovered the role of probability in radioactivity in this way, for in 1899 he did not yet have any way to observe single transmutation events (it was several years later that his research student, Hans Geiger, invented the Geiger counter). Rutherford noticed that when the total intensity of the radioactivity was graphed as a function of time, a curve like that in Figure 3.1 resulted; this is called an exponential curve. The most marked characteristic of such a curve is that it falls vertically from any value whatever to half that value in a fixed horizontal distance. This meant in Rutherford's experiment that a definite fixed time was needed for the radioactivity to diminish in intensity by half, regardless of the initial intensity. This fixed time is called the half life of the material.

What Rutherford knew and what we can here only state without proof is that the exponential curve results from the action of a law of probability on the individual radioactive-decay events. For each single nucleus, the half life represents a halfway point in probability. The chance that the nucleus will decay in less time is one half; the chance that it will decay after a longer time is one half. When this probabilistic law acts separately on a large collection of identical nuclei, the total rate of radioactive decay falls smoothly downward along an exponential curve. The same is true in the particle world. Each of the mean lives* appearing in Table 1 was measured by studying the exponential curve of decay for particles

---

* In general a mean life, or average life, is not the same as a half life. In 1950, for example, the average life expectancy (mean life) of an American male was 66.3 years, but his half life was some four years greater. He would need to reach an age of 70.7 years in order to outlive half of his contemporaries. In the particle world, on the other hand, the half life is considerably less than the mean life (0.694 is the exact factor relating them). A neutron, with a mean life of 17 minutes, has outlived half of its contemporary neutrons after 12 minutes.

of that kind. (The times themselves are usually not measured directly, but they can be inferred by measuring the speeds of the particles and the distances traveled.)

The span of known half lives from the shortest to the longest is unimaginably great. At one extreme are the super-short-lived particles, or resonances with half lives of 10^{-20} sec or less. The more

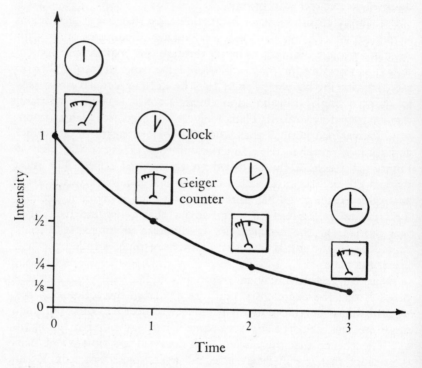

Figure 3.1. The way in which the total intensity of a radioactive sample decreases with time.

respectable particles (Table 1) live from 10^{-10} sec up to some minutes—except, of course, for the stable particles which, as far as we know, live forever. Radioactive nuclei are known with half lives ranging from about 10^{-3} sec up to 3×10^{10} years. Regardless of the half life, the decay of every unstable particle follows the same inexorable exponential curve.

The radioactivity created by nuclear explosions consists of a mixture of many different radioactive species, so that the fallout subsequent to bomb tests does not follow a single simple exponential curve. Some of the radioactive nuclei decay so quickly after the explosion—within seconds or minutes—that they contaminate only a local region and are not a public-health problem. Other species have such a long half life—millions of years—that their rate of decay remains always very small. In between are the nuclei with half lives of a few years up to a few thousand years; these constitute the potential hazard of fallout. The often-discussed Co^{60} (cobalt sixty) has a half life of 5.3 years, and Sr^{90} (strontium ninety) a half life of 28 years. The isotope of carbon, C^{14}, which has been so useful for dating archaeological finds because of its half life of 5770 years, is also formed in the atmosphere by bomb tests. This will greatly complicate, perhaps invalidate altogether, the C^{14} dating method for archaeologists of future millenia.

We have concentrated on the probability of *time* which determines the characteristic decay pattern of unstable particles and nuclei. Probability also manifests itself in other ways in the submicroscopic world. There is the probability of "branching ratio." A kaon may decay in various ways: into two pions or into a muon and a neutrino, among other possibilities. Which branch any particular kaon will choose to follow is completely indeterminate, but the probability for each branch is readily measurable (given enough kaons). There is also a probability of scattering. If one particle flies close to another, it may be deflected. Quantum mechanics permits only the calculation of the probability of a certain deflection, never the certainty of a deflection.

A particularly fascinating aspect of probability at the fundamental level is the phenomenon of "tunneling." If a particle is held on one side of a wall which, according to classical physics, is totally impenetrable, there is a certain chance that it will emerge on the other side. The alpha decay of nuclei can be explained as a tunneling phenomenon. The alpha particle is held within the nucleus by an "impenetrable" wall of electrical force. Yet, with a certain small probability, it may pop through the wall and fly away to be recorded by someone's Geiger counter. The chance that a man leaning idly against the wall of his hotel room will suddenly find himself in the next room is fortunately much smaller than the chance that an alpha particle will escape from the nucleus. If the man leaned patiently for a billion years, the probability of his tunneling through would be entirely negligible. Students in dull lectures should therefore put no hope in the tunneling phenomenon as a way to emerge into the room below. Tunneling helps particles get out of sticky situations, but has no direct impact on man.

We conclude this section with some general remarks about probability. First, not *every* aspect of nature is uncertain and probabilistic. Many of the properties of stable systems—say the spin of an electron or its mass—are precisely defined. Even where a law of probability is at work, the probability of an event may be so close to zero or to one that its nonoccurrence or occurrence can be regarded in practice as a certainty. The chance that the tunneling phenomenon will be experienced by a man can be said to be effectively zero. The chance that a proton will decay in a billion years is essentially zero (this has been measured). The chance that a pion will live for two hours is as good as zero. Because quantummechanical probabilities in the macroscopic world are always so close to zero or one, the deterministic laws of classical physics are completely adequate and accurate for describing large-scale phenomena.

Is the probability of the submicroscopic world really a fundamental probability of nature, or is it perhaps, after all, a probability of ignorance, arising out of a complicated deeper, as yet undiscovered, substructure of matter? Much heated discussion has raged around this question. The simplest answer which can be given is: "No one knows." Most scientists regard it as not a very interesting question. Since nothing of a deeper substructure is known, it is not fruitful at this moment in history to discuss it. So far as we know now, the probability is indeed fundamental, but one need cling to this idea no more firmly than to any other in science.

Nevertheless, some of the greatest scientists of this century did find the question interesting and have discussed it. Those arguing for the fundamental nature of the laws of probability have a bit better time of it, for they have all of the successes of quantum mechanics on their side. Those favoring the view that the probability of quantum mechanics is really a probability of ignorance can adduce at best philosophic, and not scientific, arguments. Einstein, for example, liked to remark that he did not believe in God playing dice, and in 1953 he wrote,* "In my opinion it is deeply unsatisfying to base physics on such a theoretical outlook, since relinquishing the possibility of an objective description . . . cannot but cause one's picture of the physical world to dissolve into a fog."

The arguments in favor of the truly fundamental role of probability in nature are more subtle, being based on the theory of quantum mechanics. We shall give just one here. The manufacturers of baseballs try hard to make all of their balls identical. It is, of course, an impossible task. No two can ever be precisely alike down to the last microscopic detail, because each ball is a complicated structure with many constituents—more than 10^{25} constituents if we count atoms. On the other hand, there is pretty good evidence that any two electrons are, in fact, truly identical, and that relatively few parameters are required to specify an electron completely. In short, the electron seems to be a decidedly much more elementary structure than a baseball. This is not a trivial conclusion. If there were infinitely many layers of nature to uncover, the electron could just as well be about as complex as the baseball. Since the electron follows laws of probability, one is led to suspect that these laws are themselves of an elementary and fundamental kind, not merely a reflection of the fact that a complicated unknown structure resides within the electron.

Although arguments of this kind sound scientific, they are no more rigorous than Einstein's statement of belief. We can only wait and see.

Annihilation and Creation

Nineteenth-century chemistry was based solidly on two laws of conservation: the conservation of mass and the conservation of energy. The theory of relativity at the beginning of this century showed that mass was, in principle, convertible into energy and energy into mass. It did not say that mass *must* be created or annihilated, only that it could be. But nature, like a dog on a leash, has a way of doing everything not absolutely forbidden to it. The

---

* A. Einstein, in *Scientific Papers Presented to Max Born* (New York: Hafner Publishing Company, Inc., 1953), p. 40. Original in German.

discovery of the positron in 1932 provided the first clear evidence of the creation of mass, and Fermi's theory of beta decay shortly afterward showed that the electrons emitted in beta radioactivity must be created on the spot. Quantum mechanics had, in the meantime, provided a theoretical framework for dealing with mass creation, in particular, showing that the creation of a photon of light energy does not differ in any essential way from the creation of a material particle. By the mid thirties, creation and annihilation of material particles was a well-established fact. Now we recognize that any and all particles may be created or annihilated. All of the unstable particles undergo spontaneous annihilation, the stable particles can be annihilated only by coming into contact with their antiparticles. When enough energy is at hand, any particle, stable or unstable, may be created.

The decay of an unstable particle is the simplest example illustrating both annihilation and creation of mass. Some typical decay modes are listed in Table 1. In the beta decay of the neutron, written

$$n \rightarrow p + e^- + \overline{\nu_e},$$

a neutron is annihilated, and a proton, an electron, and an antineutrino are created. This is the only way in which a neutron may decay, except for the rare case in which it also emits a photon. A kaon, on the other hand, has a variety of decay modes. The positively charged kaon, for example, can vanish in the following ways:

$$K^+ \rightarrow \pi^+ + \pi^0 \qquad (21\%)$$
$$K^+ \rightarrow \mu^+ + \nu_\mu \qquad (63\%)$$
$$K^+ \rightarrow \pi^+ + \pi^+ + \pi^- \qquad (5.5\%)$$
$$K^+ \rightarrow \pi^+ + \pi^0 + \pi^0 \qquad (1.7\%)$$
$$K^+ \rightarrow e^+ + \nu_e \qquad (\text{rare})$$
$$K^+ \rightarrow \mu^+ + \nu_\mu + \pi^0 \qquad (3.4\%)$$
$$K^+ \rightarrow e^+ + \nu_e + \pi^0 \qquad (4.8\%)$$
$$K^+ \rightarrow e^+ + \nu_e + \pi^+ + \pi^- \qquad (\text{rare})$$
$$K^+ \rightarrow \text{any of the above} + \gamma \qquad (\text{rare}).$$

(Because of experimental errors, the percentages do not add up exactly to 100.) The symbols π (pi), μ (mu), and ν (nu) stand for the pion, muon, and neutrino; the charge of the particle, if any, is indicated by a superscript. The electron is represented by e, e^+ being the positron, or antielectron. The photon is designated by γ

(gamma) because high-energy photons are frequently called γ rays.*

An interesting decay is that of the neutral pion, in which mass is transformed entirely into energy (two massless photons):

$$\pi^0 \to \gamma + \gamma.$$

A neutral pion decay is shown in Figure 3.2. Total annihilation of mass also occurs when particle meets antiparticle, for instance, electron plus positron:

$$e^+ + e^- \to \gamma + \gamma.$$

Spontaneous decays and particle-antiparticle annihilation are "downhill" events. The mass of the product particles is always less than the mass of the initial particle or particles, and the difference is converted into energy of motion imparted to the product particles. "Uphill" events, in which new mass is created, can be stimulated by the use of high-speed projectile particles, either furnished free in the cosmic radiation, or furnished at great expense by man-made accelerators. If two protons collide, new and/or heavier particles may be created. Pions are produced by the reaction,

$$p + p \to p + n + \pi^+.$$

Lambda particles and kaons may be produced by the reaction

$$p + p \to p + \Lambda^0 + K^+.$$

These are both common reactions which occur when one proton (the projectile) is fired at high speed at another proton (the target). In practice, the target might be a container of hydrogen atoms (whose nuclei are protons). The mass of the particles created exceeds the mass of the colliding particles. The kinetic energy of the projectile has supplied the energy needed to create the extra mass. A pion created in this way may itself be used as a projectile for further work of mass creation, as in the reaction:

$$\pi^+ + p \to \Sigma^+ + K^+.$$

---

* The high-speed particles emerging from radioactive nuclei were originally called alpha, beta, and gamma rays (α, β, and γ) when it was learned that there were three kinds (1898–1900), but before their nature was known. Later (1900–1910) α particles were discovered to be helium nuclei, two protons and two neutrons bound together; β particles were discovered to be electrons; and γ rays were discovered to be photons. The original names, nevertheless, have stuck.

When relativity swept away the law of mass conservation, it swept away the picture of a solid and reliable material basis of the universe. The modern picture is much more tenuous. Most of the material particles do not live long enough to be of any use for

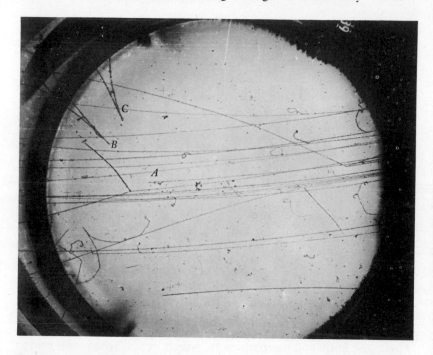

Figure 3.2. Creation and annihilation of material particles. At point A, a negative pion incident from the right collides with a proton to produce a neutral pion and a neutron: $\pi^- + p \rightarrow \pi^0 + n$. Neither of these neutral particles leaves a visible track, nor do the photons created by the immediate decay of the pion: $\pi^0 \rightarrow \gamma + \gamma$. But these two photons make their presence known at points B and C by creating electron-positron pairs, $\gamma \rightarrow e^- + e^+$. Electrons and positrons fly off at the upper left, leaving trails pointing backward to the point of the original collision, revealing the course of the photons.

building the world. Even those that do can be annihilated if struck by other energetic particles or if brought into contact with their antiparticles. The modern picture might be described as follows: Because of certain conservation laws, a very few of nature's particles happen by chance to be stable. Even these are not indestructible, but because where we live the flux of projectile particles is very low, and because our corner of the universe happens to contain a lot of matter and very little antimatter, the stable particles can form a material world which is lasting.

Waves and Particles

In the world of the very small, waves and particles appear to be not merely closely related, but actually one and the same thing— or, more accurately stated, different aspects of one and the same thing. This remarkable fact was first implied by Einstein's theory of the photon in 1905, and came to be fully appreciated after the work of de Broglie, Schrödinger, and others on the quantum theory twenty years later. Now we recognize the wave nature of matter as the thing that gives atoms their size, "explains" the uncertainty principle (to be discussed below), elucidates the role of probability in nature, and thwarts man's efforts to study the interior of elementary particles.

The concept of a particle, however small the particle may be, is easy to grasp. We can picture a golf ball and imagine it shrunk down to elementary-particle size, say 10^{-13} cm. We see in our mind's eye a tiny spherical lump of matter. It has mass; it is located at some definite point; it can move from one place to another at some measurable speed. Energy is required to set it in motion, and it gives up energy when slowed down or stopped. Picturing a massless particle that always shoots about at the speed of light is a bit harder. The massless particles in fact have a very special fascination of their own and we shall devote Chapter Five to the photon and the neutrinos. Here we shall stick to more conventional material particles to illustrate the wave-particle duality.

The concept of a wave is a bit more nebulous than that of particle, but is by no means unfamiliar. Everyone is familiar with water waves, and has at least heard of sound waves. Most children have done crude experiments with waves, snapping one end of a stretched rope or a garden hose and watching a wave travel the length of it. At first thought, waves seem to be different from particles in every way. A particle is located exactly at some point; a wave is spread out over a region of space without clear-cut boundaries. It can not be said to be located just here or there. It is hard to think of mass being associated with a wave; a wave is not a "thing," but rather a spread-out disturbance. In short, a particle has mass, can be located at a definite point, and can be imagined to have a definite size; a wave is massless, is necessarily spread out, and has an ill-defined size. Moreover, the quantities used to characterize a wave—its amplitude, wavelength, and frequency—are quantities which seem to have no meaning for particles. Picture water waves rolling toward a beach. The amplitude is the height of a crest above the mean water level; the wavelength is the distance from one crest to the next; and the frequency is the number of waves that pass a fixed point in one second. (For water waves, this could be less than one wave per second. For the standard musical A, it is 440 waves per second; for the radio waves of WCRB, Waltham, Massachusetts, it is 1,330,000 waves per second.)

In spite of these obvious differences, quantum mechanics has succeeded in merging the ideas of waves and particles. To make the merger reasonable, let us consider those properties waves and particles do have in common, even in our macroscopic world. First of all, both obviously can travel from one place to another, and at a definite speed. Here, too, there is a difference, though. The speed of a wave usually depends very little on its wavelength or its amplitude. Fortunately for the listener at the back of the second balcony at a symphony concert, sound travels at a nearly fixed speed, regardless of its loudness (amplitude) or its pitch (frequency). Particles, on the other hand, can easily be caused to travel at different speeds, dependent on their energy. Most important as a point of similarity, waves and particles can do the same job. Each can carry energy from one point to another. Each can receive energy, carry it elsewhere, and transmit it to something else. If two boys hold the ends of a long rope (see Figure 3.3), one can supply energy by shaking his end. A wave will run along the rope and transmit an impulse to the hand of the other boy. Alternatively, the same amount of energy could have been transferred by means of a "particle" such as a baseball thrown from one boy to the other.

Even today, physicists do not say that a wave *is* a particle. Rather, they express it in this way: Waves have particlelike properties; particles have wavelike properties, and the two concepts are inseparably linked. Like enlightened blind men feeling an elephant, scientists now recognize that the structures we call particles can

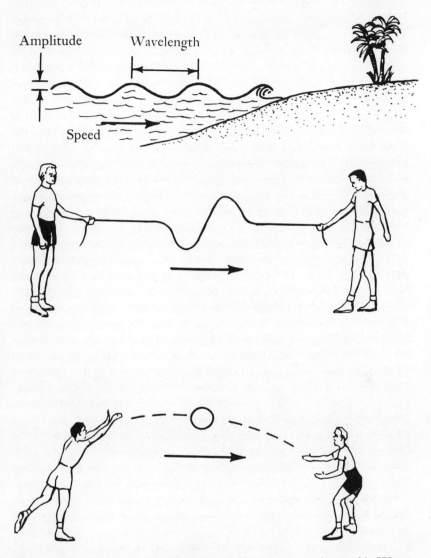

Figure 3.3. Waves and "particles" in the macroscopic world. Water waves rolling toward a beach are characterized by wavelength, amplitude, speed, and frequency (not shown). A rope wave has the same characteristics but is more localized. It can transmit energy from one boy to the other just as a thrown ball (or "particle") can.

exhibit quite different properties depending on how they are examined.

The merging of the ideas of wave and particle was made possible only by some changes in our view of waves and of particles. Both concepts have had to yield a little in order to grow more alike. Our usual picture of waves is a vibration of something. Water waves need water, sound waves need air, the rope wave needs a rope. Light waves seem to require a less substantial material, for light propagates readily through empty space. But it was naturally assumed that *something* must be vibrating in a light wave, and that something was called the ether. The efforts—all unsuccessful—to detect the ether, mostly in the latter part of the nineteenth century, form a fascinating chapter of the history of science. It is mainly to Einstein that we owe the eventual abandonment of our belief in the undetectable ether. Light waves, said Einstein, have to be regarded not as the vibrations of an underlying ether, but as the wavelike propagation through truly empty space of a tenuous substance called a "field." This may sound like a very dubious advance of science. One hypothetical substance, the "ether," is replaced by another hypothetical substance, the "field." In fact, it was an exceedingly important advance. On the technical side, the field is much better defined than the ether. A field is a quantitative concept, definable and measurable like mass or length or time, and satisfying equations of an exact theory. Quite aside from this, the sweeping away of the ether provided a dramatic change in our view of the universe. The wave becomes a more material thing, an entity by itself. It is still spread out, still characterized by wavelength and frequency and amplitude, but it is something by itself, not just the name given to a vibration of an underlying medium. It is as if the boys could transmit a rope wave without a rope. This is obviously a big step in the direction of making a wave more particlelike, an unattached bundle of energy.

Quantum mechanics then brought with it some necessary changes in our view of particles which rendered them less distinct and therefore more wavelike. The most essential feature is the nonlocalizability of particles. According to the uncertainty principle, which lies at the core of quantum mechanics, the location of a particle can never be precisely specified. The particle therefore loses its distinctness, becoming spread out and a bit fuzzy like a wave. The bigger the particle, the less important is this fuzziness, so that in the world of our senses all "particles" appear to be perfectly localized and have well-defined, sharp boundaries. In the world of the very small the fuzziness becomes all important. The fact that the hydrogen atom is 100,000 times larger than the proton at its center comes about entirely because of the nonlocalizability of the very light-weight electron which refuses to sit quietly alongside the proton, requiring instead, all of this extra space for its domain of motion.

We can say that particles are nonlocalizable because they are wavelike (which is the usual interpretation) rather than that they are wavelike because they are nonlocalizable. It does not really matter which we say, but it is somewhat simpler to take the wave nature of the particle as basic, and derive from that the other new features of quantum mechanics. The single key equation that specifies the wave nature of a particle was first postulated by Louis de Broglie in 1924; shortly afterward it was incorporated into the full theory of quantum mechanics. That the photon was in some sense both wave and particle had been known since 1905. De Broglie was the first to suggest that *every* particle should have a wave nature.

The de Broglie relation may be written in the following way:

$$\lambda = \frac{h}{p}.$$

This equation looks simple enough but has consequences as significant as Einstein's famous $E = mc^2$. First, some definitions: λ is a wavelength; h is Planck's constant; and p is momentum. The usual definition of momentum is $p = mv$, mass times velocity. Either by being heavier or by going faster, a particle acquires more momentum. A freight car moving at 10 miles per hour has more momentum than an automobile going at the same speed and, in consequence, is harder to stop. A car traveling at 60 miles per hour has more momentum than a similar car traveling at 10 miles per hour, and is again harder to stop. Roughly, the momentum of an object is a measure of how long and how hard it would need to be pushed to bring it up to its speed. Elementary particles, even when traveling near the speed of light, have very little momentum—far less, say, than a snail making its way across the floor—because of their extremely small mass. According to relativity the formula for momentum is not so simple as $p = mv$,* but the general meaning

---

* For the record, the relativistic formula is $p = mv/\sqrt{1 - v^2/c^2}$ for particles with mass m, where c is the speed of light. For particles with no mass it is $p = E/c$, where E is the energy of the particle.

of momentum is the same. Note in particular that a photon or neutrino with *no* mass can have momentum.

The momentum p is a particlelike property. The wavelength is obviously a wavelike property. The de Broglie equation links these two properties, and the link tying them together is Planck's constant h. It is the small size of this quantum constant h that makes the wave properties of particles irrelevant except in the world of the very small. Just as with Einstein's equation, $E = mc^2$, where the heart of the equation is the proportionality of the energy E to the mass m, the factor c^2 being a constant of proportionality, so with de Broglie's equation, the heart of the equation is the proportionality of wavelength λ to $1/p$, the *inverse* of the momentum p, Planck's constant h being the constant of proportionality. The equation says that any particle whatever with a momentum p has an associated wave of wavelength λ which is given by the formula $\lambda = h/p$. Because p is "downstairs" (in the denominator), larger p implies smaller λ. For the enormous momenta of macroscopic objects, the associated wavelength is so small that the wave property is completely unobservable. A man walking at three miles per hour has a wavelength of less than 10^{-33} cm. If he tried to move more slowly in order to have a larger wavelength it would not help much. Progressing at one centimeter per century he would have a wavelength of less than 10^{-21} cm, still one hundred million times smaller than the size of an elementary particle. On the other hand, a single electron moving at about 3×10^8 cm/sec in the hydrogen atom has a wavelength of 2×10^{-8} cm, just about the diameter of the hydrogen atom. We shall return to the question of wavelength and localizability.

To learn an equation and to appreciate and understand it are two different things. Anyone can commit to memory in a few moments the equations $E = mc^2$ and $\lambda = h/p$, but what do these equations really mean? Why are they so significant? As an aid to learning to "feel" their meaning, it is instructive to compare them. The first is one of the fundamental equations of relativity; the second is a fundamental equation of quantum mechanics. The first contains the universal constant c, the speed of light, which is basic to the theory of relativity (recall that c is nature's speed limit, and that the "peculiar" features of relativity become evident near this speed). The second equation contains the universal constant h, Planck's constant, which is basic to the theory of quantum mechanics (recall, for example, that the spins of elementary particles are measured in units of $h/2\pi$). In Einstein's equation, E and m are called variables for, unlike c, they can take on different values for different particles. Similarly, λ and p are the variables of de Broglie's equation. Most important for providing new insights into nature, both equations perform a synthesis. Mass and energy, previously thought to be distinct and unrelated quantities, are drawn together into a simple relation of proportionality by Einstein's equation. De Broglie's equation performs an analogous synthesis of the apparently unrelated ideas of wavelength and particle momentum. The position of the variables in the equation is, of course, also of the utmost significance. The appearance of m "upstairs" in Einstein's equation means that more mass has more energy, or conversely, the creation of a larger mass requires a larger energy. The fact that p occurs "downstairs" in de Broglie's equation means that a particle with more momentum has a shorter associated wavelength. The lighter a particle and the more slowly it moves, the greater its wavelength will be; therefore, the more evident its wavelike properties will be.

Also significant are the magnitudes of the constants: c is "large" and h is "small" relative to the "normal" magnitudes of our everyday macroscopic world. Thinking in our self-centered human terms then, a little mass corresponds to a great deal of energy, because m is multiplied by the "big" number c^2 in Einstein's equation. What we regard as the enormous energy release of an atomic bomb comes from the conversion to energy of not very much mass, about 1 gm, for a Hiroshima-sized bomb. On the same human scale of magnitudes, h is very small. A "normal" momentum, therefore, corresponds to an infinitesimal wavelength. The size of these constants is related to the late appearance on the human scene of the theories of relativity and quantum mechanics. Just *because* the fundamental constants of these theories are so far removed from normal human experience, man could never have discovered the theories until his experimental technique extended his observation far beyond the normal range of human perception.

The fact that light waves are absorbed only in discrete bundles of energy, photons, provided the first evidence that waves have a particlelike property (Einstein, 1905). Since then there have been many pieces of evidence, a few direct, but most of them indirect, confirming the wave nature of particles. The decay of the neutral pion (Figure 3.2) provides an explosive kind of link between waves and particles. A material particle, the π^0, is converted wholly into light waves (two photons) which, in turn, give rise to particles when they vanish.

The most convincing direct evidence of waves comes through the phenomena of diffraction and interference. Diffraction is the slight bending and distortion of a wave that occurs as it passes an obstacle. A particle, on the other hand, merely passing near an obstacle, should be uninfluenced. If two beams of waves come together they may interfere, that is, tend to cancel each other, if the crest of one wave happens to match the trough of the other. Such interference is purely a wave phenomenon and cannot be imagined for two beams of particles. The observation of these effects of diffraction and interference can be regarded as convincing evidence for waves—as the nearest we can come to "seeing" the waves of the submicroscopic world. It was, in fact, through the study of these two effects that the wave theory of light became firmly established in the early part of the nineteenth century. Figure 3.4 shows some patterns of diffraction and interference of light.

Following de Broglie's suggestion that all particles should show wavelike behavior, Clinton Davisson and Lester Germer discovered the wavelike effects of diffraction and interference in electron beams (1927). More recently, neutrons have proved to be the best particles for demonstrating the phenomena of diffraction and interference. A book by Donald Hughes, a pioneer in exhibiting the wave properties of particles, is entitled simply *Neutron Optics;** this title provides eloquent testimony to the merger between waves and particles which has occurred in physics. The particular merit of the neutron is that it carries no electric charge. The most marked wave effects occur for the greatest wavelength which, in turn— according to the de Broglie equation—requires the least momentum. Electrons of low momentum are easily disturbed by any small electric forces which they encounter; thus they cannot penetrate solid matter. But neutrons can be slowed down to a walk, 10^5 cm/sec (about 2,200 miles per hour) or less, without being readily subject to disturbing influences. These slow neutrons, with a relatively long wavelength, pass easily through thin layers of solid

---

* D. J. Hughes, *Neutron Optics* (New York: Interscience Publishers, Inc., 1953).

material. As a bench mark for the wavelength-momentum relationship, we note that a neutron moving at 9,000 miles per hour, or 4×10^5 cm/sec—about half the speed of an orbital astronaut—has a wavelength of one Angstrom unit (10^{-8} cm).

A surprising number of facts about the elementary-particle world can be understood in terms of the wave nature of particles. Perhaps

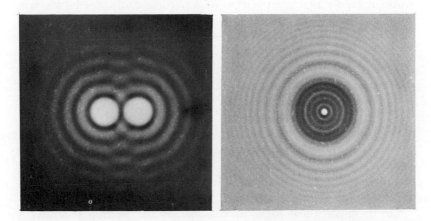

Figure 3.4. Interference and diffraction of light. Two sources of light shining through the same circular hole made the pattern on the left. Where the two waves coincide, crest to crest and trough to trough, they reinforce each other producing a bright band. Where they coincide crest to trough, they "interfere" and cancel each other to give a dark band. On the right is the shadow of a circular disk. Waves passing near the edge of the disk are diffracted and the shadow is not sharp. Waves bent inward to the center of the shadow from all sides of the disk reinforce each other and produce a bright spot.

the most essential fact about a wave, as far as the world of particles is concerned, is its nonlocalizability. A wave cannot be said to be exactly at this point or exactly at that point. At best it is known to be in this region or that region. It can be *approximately* localized, but the crucial distance below which it makes no sense to speak of the position of a wave is its own wavelength. Crudely speaking, a wave has to go through at least one cycle of oscillation in order to be a wave at all, and therefore it must occupy a space at least as big as its own wavelength. Picture, for example, a long rope which has been given a single shake at one end. A wave in the shape of a single hump will run along the rope; the position of the hump marks the position of the wave. But the wave occupies a region, not a point, and the size of the region is the length of the hump, which is roughly the wavelength of the disturbance.

The relevance of this nonlocalizability in the submicroscopic world is simply that the position of a particle can never be known, even in principle, to greater accuracy than the wavelength of the particle. The wave nature of matter introduces an essential fuzziness into nature; the particle wavelength defines a region of uncertainty, within which the whereabouts of the particle is unknown and unknowable. One might think this should permit us to dispense with particles altogether and say that there are only waves. This cannot be done, for the particle property is still evident in processes of change, that is, in events of annihilation and creation. The birth and death of particles is "particlelike," occurring suddenly at one point in space and time; the life of particles between creation and annihilation is "wavelike," characterized by a wavelength and diffused over a region of space.

Let us apply these ideas to the size of the hydrogen atom. A hydrogen atom consists of one proton, a heavy particle which we may think of for the moment as being fixed at a certain point, and one electron, a light particle moving about the proton. Between them acts an attractive electric force. According to "classical" ideas, the electron should emit light waves, gradually lose energy, and spiral down into the proton, so that the size of the atom would finally be about the size of the proton, 10^{-13} cm.* It is the wave nature of the electron which prevents this collapse. If the electron spiraled into the proton, it would be confined to a smaller and smaller region of space, which means that its associated wavelength would have to become smaller and smaller. According to the de Broglie equation smaller wavelength means larger momentum, which in turn means more energy of motion (kinetic energy). This

---

* The thoughtful reader might translate this situation to the solar system, and wonder why the earth, which is described by classical laws, does not spiral into the sun. The answer: It does! The difference, an all-important one, is a matter of time. The electron should spiral into the proton in about 10^{-8} sec, the earth into the sun in about 10^{24} years (recall that the known lifetime of the universe is only about 10^{10} years).

is the crux of the matter. The wave nature of the electron means that it can be confined to a small region of space only if it has a high kinetic energy. Beyond a certain point the force of electrical attraction is not sufficient to supply the needed energy and the electron stops its inward motion. Another way to say this is the following: Because of the electrical attraction, the electron "wants" to be near the proton. But in order to have the smallest possible energy, it "wants" to have a very large wavelength and be spread over a large region of space. These two opposing influences—the proton's force tending to pull it in, its wave nature tending to push it out—reach a point of balance at a certain distance; this distance happens to be about 10^{-8} cm and determines the size of the atom. The size of all the heavier atoms is determined in a similar way and they are all about 10^{-8} cm in diameter. The same argument, incidentally, was used to banish electrons from the nucleus. An electron confined to the small size of the nucleus would have too much energy and could not be held there. An electron that shoots out of the nucleus in beta decay, therefore, must have been formed at the moment of decay, and not been supplied from a reservoir of electrons already there.

The wave nature of particles is intimately connected with the fundamental role of probability in nature. This relation is not easy to understand in all its ramifications, but the hydrogen atom will serve again to illustrate the general idea. In the atom, the electron cannot be thought of as existing at any particular point, but must be visualized in terms of waves. It is spread diffusely over a region of about one wavelength. Yet we can do an experiment to reveal the electron as a particle. If a high-speed positron is fired at the atom it may strike the electron; if it does so, both will vanish and a pair of photons will emerge. These photons could, in principle, be studied to reveal the place within the atom where the electron was at the moment of its annihilation. (This does not happen to be a practical experiment, but it is all right in principle.) The resolution of the apparent paradox of the electron wave and the electron particle comes through the concept of probability. Before the annihilation event, the electron wave must be interpreted as a wave of probability. Where the wave is large (or strong) there is a good chance of finding the electron. Where the wave is small (or weak) there is a very small chance of finding the electron. If the same experiment with the positron is repeated with a number of hydrogen atoms, each one *exactly* the same as each other one in every property we know how to specify, the results of the different experiments will not be the same. Sometimes the electron will be found in one part of the atom, sometimes in another; sometimes close to the nucleus, sometimes far away; but it will almost always be found within about 10^{-8} cm of the proton, within the region where the electron wave was large. In general, for any particle, the "fuzziness" contributed by its wave nature is related to a distribution of probability for that particle.

One of the most important insights into nature revealed by quantum mechanics is the Heisenberg uncertainty principle. This is a general principle that takes many forms, but it will be sufficient to consider one of its forms, which can be written

$$(\Delta x)(\Delta p) = \hbar.$$

On the right side is $\hbar$, the ubiquitous Planck's constant (here divided by 2π) which turns up in every equation of quantum mechanics. Momentum is again represented by p, and position (distance) is indicated by x. The Δ symbols mean "uncertainty of": Δx is the uncertainty of position, Δp is the uncertainty of momentum. The product of these two uncertainties is equal to the constant $\hbar$. Now $\hbar$ is, on the human scale, a very small quantity, so that Δx and Δp can be so close to zero in the macroscopic world that there is for all practical purposes no uncertainty whatever in the position and momentum of large objects. If we want to specify a man's position to within the size of a single atom, his speed could, in principle, be determined to an accuracy of about 10^{-24} cm/sec. Needless to say, the inaccuracies of measurement take over long before the inherent fundamental limitation of accuracy implied by the uncertainty relation can play any role. But in the world of particles, this is not so. Masses and distances are so small that the uncertainty principle is of vital importance. An electron, for example, in order to be localized within an atom, 10^{-8} cm (which is equivalent to assigning it this great an uncertainty of position), has an inherent uncertainty of speed of about 10^8 cm/sec.

The uncertainty principle, when discussed by itself outside the framework of quantum mechanics, is often assigned a profundity and depth which are probably unjustified. It has obvious philosophic implications and is especially popular with those who wish to attack science, for it shows that even the "exact" scientist is prohibited by nature from measuring things as exactly as he might like. One might also argue that nature is shielding her innermost secrets by allowing man to proceed only so far and no farther in his downward quest. In truth, the uncertainty principle is fundamental and presents in capsule form an important part of the physical content of quantum mechanics. Nevertheless, it may be viewed as just one more aspect of the wave nature of matter, in which case it seems considerably less mysterious.

Suppose we turn to sound waves, which are more familiar than particle waves, and consider the array of pipes connected to a large organ. In a typical open pipe, the crest of a wave is located at the lower end and a trough at the upper end, so that one half of a wavelength is confined within the pipe. The large pipes produce low tones of long wavelength, the short pipes produce high tones of short wavelength.

We can ask: If the air in one pipe is set vibrating, where is the sound wave in the pipe? It is, of course, everywhere within the pipe; its location cannot be more accurately specified. We can say that the length of the pipe is the "uncertainty of position" of the sound wave. The high tone is rather accurately located in a small pipe, the low tone is much less accurately located in the long pipe. Since the length of the pipe is half the wavelength, we can express our conclusions in the following very simple equation:

$$\Delta x = \frac{1}{2}\lambda,$$

the uncertainty of position of the sound wave is one half of its wavelength. The factor $\frac{1}{2}$ arose from the particular example of open organ pipes. In some other example it might be a different factor, but will never be far from one. As a more general approximate rule we can write

$$\Delta x = \lambda.$$

But this is just a mathematical expression for the principle of non-localizability we have already used to discuss the size of the hydrogen atom. Any wave must occupy a region of space at least as great as its own wavelength.

Now let us return to particle waves and do a little algebra. If Δx, the uncertainty of position of a wave, is equal to λ, the wavelength, and, according to the de Broglie equation for particle waves, λ is equal to h/p, then Δx is equal to h/p; that is,

$$\Delta x = \frac{h}{p}.$$

This equation may be rewritten in the form,

$$(\Delta x)p = h.$$

In words, the uncertainty of position of a particle-wave multiplied by the momentum of the particle is equal to Planck's constant h. Actually this equation is not quite correct, and the p must be replaced by $2\pi\Delta p$, to make it

$$2\pi(\Delta x)(\Delta p) = h \quad \text{or} \quad (\Delta x)(\Delta p) = \hbar,$$

precisely the equation we wrote originally for the uncertainty principle. The reason for the last-minute shift from p to $2\pi\Delta p$ is a technical point* that does not change the picture. The essential point is that the Heisenberg uncertainty principle is a consequence of the wave nature of particles. It is no more profound, and in this form says no more and no less than the de Broglie equation giving the wavelength of material particles. Uncertainty of measurement arises essentially from the nonlocalizability of waves.

It is true that the uncertainty principle makes life hard for the elementary-particle physicist, and expensive for the governments of the world. Our knowledge of the world of the very small comes mainly from the results of "scattering" experiments, in which projectile particles are fired at target nuclei, where they are deflected, or scattered, and re-emerge to be observed with Geiger counters, bubble chambers, or other detectors. More complicated things than deflection may occur in these collisions; for instance, new particles may be created and also emerge. Scattering has come to be used to describe the general process in which two or more particles come together and, after a brief interaction, various particles fly apart. Man must infer what happened in the brief moment of interaction and over the tiny distances when the particles were close together by studying in detail the particles that emerge from the collisions—what particles they are, how fast they travel, and which way they go. One important limitation on the accuracy with which he can do this is imposed by the wave nature of the particles.

Suppose we wanted to study ships in a harbor by analyzing waves

---

* A perfectly well-defined momentum in quantum mechanics requires a wave that goes through many cycles of oscillation. In order to get a wave as localized as possible and to have it go through just one or very few cycles of oscillation, it is necessary to "mix" different momenta or, in other words, to have an uncertainty of momentum.

that passed them. Waves rolling past a large ship at anchor would be strongly affected. The ship would leave a "shadow" of calm water and the waves rounding the ends of the ship would be diffracted in a characteristic way. We could learn the shape and size of the ship fairly accurately by studying waves that had passed it in various directions. If, on the other hand, the same waves rolled by a piece of piling sticking out of the water, they would scarcely be affected and would at most show that some small thing was there, without revealing its size or shape. But we should have no difficulty analyzing the piling with light waves, that is, by looking at it. The essential point is this. Waves provide a good method of analysis only for objects bigger than themselves. A wave cannot reveal details any smaller than its own wavelength. Therefore, if one wants to study an object with waves, the wavelength chosen should be smaller than the object.

The "objects," or better, the small regions of space, which the physicist wants to study are now about 10^{-13} cm or less—he would be delighted if he could study much smaller regions. He therefore wants to use, as projectiles for his scattering experiment, particles whose wavelength is as small as possible. The difficulty is that, according to the de Broglie equation, small wavelength means large momentum. To probe smaller and smaller distances, the physicist must use more and more energetic particles with more and more momentum. This requires the construction of large particle accelerators; in recent years, these have become enormous and costly.

The structure of the proton has been revealed mainly through experiments carried out at Stanford University by Robert Hofstadter. At the time of the experiments, the Stanford linear accelerator pushed electrons to an energy of 600 Mev (600 million electron volts); at this energy, their wavelength is about 2×10^{-13} cm. Recall, for comparison, that the electron in the hydrogen atom has a wavelength of 2×10^{-8} cm, one hundred thousand times larger. The largest accelerators now operating, at Brookhaven, New York, and Geneva, Switzerland, each accelerate protons to an energy of about 30 billion electron volts, where their wavelengths are 4×10^{-15} cm. Still larger accelerators, and smaller wavelengths, are planned for the future, but man is up against the hard fact that he must solve the puzzles of the elementary particles, if he is to solve them at all, using wavelengths not much less than 10^{-15} cm. In order to get down to 4×10^{-15} cm, the Brookhaven machine (Figure 1.4), which is half a mile in circumference, required an exenditure of 32 million dollars, and has an annual operating budget of several million dollars. In this sense, the uncertainty principle is certainly impeding man's effort to reveal the deeper structure of nature.

More Great Ideas

Twentieth-century science has introduced a number of startling ideas—startling because they are in conflict with the common sense based on everyday observation. The three chosen for discussion in this chapter are not unique, although they are surely among the most important. Several other insights into the workings of nature which deserve to be called "great ideas" have already been cited without being so labeled. The mass-energy equivalence is one and the speed of light as the fundamental constant that is nature's speed limit is another. In discussing spin, we encountered one of the most important ideas of quantum mechanics. This is the general phenomenon of quantization or discontinuity in nature. In the macroscopic world of our senses, all physical quantities *seem* to be continuous. A piece of iron pipe can apparently be cut to any length whatever, not just six feet or eight feet or ten feet. A child's top as it is slowing down seems to decrease its rate of rotation smoothly as it gradually comes to rest. Yet we know that, viewed sufficiently closely, the pipe is composed of separate atoms, and the spin of the top is changing jerkily by integral multiple of the fundamental constant $\hbar$. An invisible speck of iron might be six atoms long or eight, but not six and a half. The spin of a top, as it slows down, makes "quantum jumps" of $\hbar$ or $2\hbar$ or $3\hbar$ but never anything in between. Only because the increment between adjacent quantum values is so extremely small on the human scale does smooth continuous variation seem to be the rule in the large scale world.

Not all of nature's quantization is understood. The reasons for discontinuity of energy and of spin are provided by the quantum theory. But why mass and charge come only in lumps of certain sizes remains a mystery and a challenge.

As a last "great idea" we mention the relativity of time. This is in some ways the most fascinating of all, for it leads to a number of apparent paradoxes in violent discord with common sense. Common sense and our entire round of daily life are based on the idea that there is a definite fixed time about which everybody can agree. This, according to the theory of relativity, is just not so. The scale of time is a slippery thing that varies with the state of motion. My time and yours are not the same if we are in a state of relative motion. But unless our relative speed gets near to the speed of light, the difference will not be noticeable.

An adequate discussion of the relativity of time would carry us too far beyond the scope of this book, but we can mention its dramatic effect on the lifetimes of elementary particles. It is found experimentally that the lifetime of a pion (and of any other particle) increases as the speed of the particle increases. Because a law of probability governs the decay, it is necessary to study many pions at each speed, and to determine an average lifetime at each speed. The results can be pictured as in Figure 3.5. For speeds that are not very great, the average lifetime remains unchanged and seems to be a well-defined constant for the pion. This is indicated by the horizontal part of the curve at speeds well below the speed of light. As the speed of light is approached, the average lifetime increases markedly. Pions moving at 80 per cent of the speed of light live (on the average) 1.67 times as long as slow pions. At 99 per cent of the speed of light, time is "dilated" by a factor of 7, and such fast pions live 7 times as long as their slow brothers. The interpretation of relativity is not that the intrinsic lifetime is really increased, but that the rate of time flow is slowed down for the high-speed particle. The fast pion lives out its allotted lifetime always the same from its own point of view but, from the point of view of the laboratory observer, more time has gone by. The internal clock of the high-speed pion becomes sluggish and by the time it has ticked off 10^{-8} sec, the laboratory clocks have briskly ticked off 7×10^{-8} sec. Such dilation of time was boldly predicted in 1905, decades before its direct measurement became possible. It might be added that high-speed travel is not the fountain of youth. Since the whole internal time scale and rhythm of life would be slowed down for a high speed traveler, he would be in no position to enjoy his extra longevity. To the traveler, his own life span would appear to be exactly normal.

The strange ideas of modern physics are very likely only a foretaste of stranger ones to come. Man's direct perceptions are limited and, as methods of observation and accompanying theories extend beyond the range of this direct perception, it should not be surprising if the ideas and ways of looking at the world which result conflict with the evidence of the senses. Just as a pilot learning to fly on instruments must learn to believe the instruments and forget his sensations, the scientist (and eventually the nonscientist, too) must learn to think in new ways and give up the preconceived

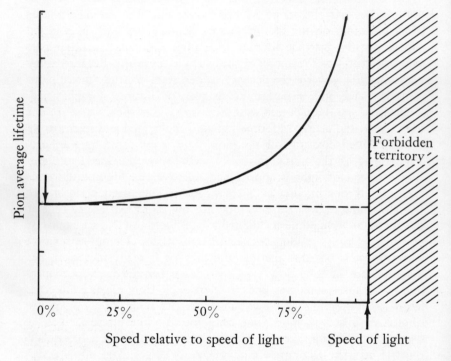

Figure 3.5. Time dilation. The lifetime of a pion increases as its speed increases. For reference, the arrow points to a speed corresponding to circling the earth in five seconds—one thousand times faster than an orbital astronaut.

notions based on past experience. The evidence of history so far suggests that man's ability to accommodate to strange new ideas and, even more important, to generate such ideas, will enable him to proceed still a long way in his quest for fundamental understanding.

Chapter Four

Conservation Laws

In a slow and subtle, yet inexorable, way conservation laws have moved in the past few centuries from the role of interesting sidelight in physics to the most central position. What little we now understand about the interactions and transformations of particles comes in large part through certain conservation laws which govern elementary-particle behavior.

A conservation law is a statement of constancy in nature. If there is a room full of people, say, at a cocktail party, and no one comes in or leaves, we can say that there is a law of conservation of the number of people; that number is a constant. This would be a rather uninteresting law. But suppose the conservation law remained valid as guests came and went. This would be more interesting, for it would imply that the rate of arrival of guests was exactly equal to the rate of departure. During a process of change, something is remaining constant. The significant conservation laws in nature are of this type, laws of constancy during change. It is not surprising that scientists, in their search for simplicity, fasten on conservation laws with particular enthusiasm, for what could be simpler than a quantity that remains absolutely constant during complicated processes of change. To cite an example from the world of particles, the total electric charge remains precisely constant in every collision, regardless of how many particles may be created or annihilated in the process.

The classical laws of physics are expressed primarily as laws of change, rather than as laws of constancy. Newton's law of motion describes how the motion of objects responds to forces that act upon them. Maxwell's equations of electromagnetism connect the rate of change of electric and magnetic fields in space and time. The early emphasis in fundamental science was rather naturally on discovering those laws which successfully describe the changes actually occurring in nature. Briefly, the "classical" philosophy concerning nature's laws is this. Man can imagine countless possible laws, indeed infinitely many, that might describe a particular phenomenon. Of these, nature has chosen only one simple law, and the job of science is to find it. Having successfully found laws of change, man may derive from them certain conservation laws, such as the conservation of energy in mechanics. These appear as particularly interesting and useful consequences of the theory, but are not themselves taken as fundamental statements of the theory.

Gradually conservation laws have percolated to the top in the hierarchy of natural laws. This is not merely because of their simplicity, although this has been an important factor. It comes about also for two other reasons. One is the connection between conservation laws and principles of invariance and symmetry in nature— surely, one of the most beautiful aspects of modern science. The meaning of this connection will be discussed near the end of this chapter. The other reason we want to discuss here might best be described simply as a new view of the world, in which conservation laws appear naturally as the most fundamental statements of natural law. This new view is a view of order upon chaos—the order of conservation laws imposed upon the chaos of continual annihilation and creation taking place in the submicroscopic world. The strong hint emerging from recent studies of elementary particles is that the only inhibition imposed upon the chaotic flux of events in the world of the very small is that imposed by the conservation laws. Everything that *can* happen without violating a conservation law *does* happen.

This new view of democracy in nature—freedom under law— represents a revolutionary change in man's view of natural law. The older view of a fundamental law of nature was that it must be a law of *permission*. It defined what *can* (and must) happen in natural phenomena. According to the new view, the more fundamental law is a law of *prohibition*. It defines what *cannot* happen. A conservation law is, in effect, a law of prohibition. It prohibits any phenomenon that would change the conserved quantity, but otherwise allows any events. Consider, for example, the production of pions in a proton-proton collision,

$$p + p \rightarrow p + p + \pi + \pi + \pi + \cdots .$$

If a law of permission were operative, one might expect that, for protons colliding in a particular way, the law would specify the number and the type of pions produced. A conservation law is less restrictive. The conservation of energy limits the number of pions that can be produced, because the mass of each one uses up some of the available energy. It might say, for example, that not more than six pions can be produced. In the actual collision there might be none, or one, or any number up to six. The law of charge conservation says that the total charge of the pions must be zero, but places no restriction on the charge of any particular pion; this could be positive, negative, or neutral.

To make more clear the distinction between laws of permission and laws of prohibition, let us return to the cocktail party. A law of change, which is a law of permission, might describe the rate of arrival and the rate of departure of guests as functions of time. In simplest form, it might say that three guests per minute arrive at 6:00, two guests per minute at 6:15, and so on. Or it might say, without changing its essential character as a law of permission, that the rate of arrival of guests is given by the formula:

$$R = \frac{A}{\pi D} \frac{1}{1 + \left(T - 5 - 2\frac{A}{D}\right)^2},$$

where R is the number of guests arriving per minute, A is the annual income of the host in thousands of dollars, D is the distance in miles from the nearest metropolitan center, and T is the time of day. This law resembles, in spirit, a classical law of physics. It covers many situations, but for any particular situation it predicts exactly what will happen.

A conservation law is simpler and less restrictive. Suppose it is observed that between 7 and 10 o'clock the number of guests is conserved at all parties. This is a grand general statement, appealing for its breadth of application and its simplicity. It would, were it true, be regarded as a deep truth, a very profound law of human behavior. But it gives much less detailed information than the formula for R above. The conservation law allows the guests to arrive at any rate whatever, so long as guests depart at the same rate. To push the analogy with natural law a bit further, we should say that according to the old view, since cocktail-party attendance is a fundamental aspect of human behavior, we seek and expect to find simple explicit laws governing the flow of guests. According to the new view, we expect to find the flux of arriving and departing guests limited only by certain conservation principles. Any behavior not prohibited by the conservation laws will, sooner or later, at some cocktail party, actually occur.

It should be clear that there is a close connection between this view of nature and the fundamental role of probability in nature. If the conservation law does not prohibit various possible results of an experiment, as in the proton-proton collision cited above, then these various possibilities will occur, each with some definite probability. The very fact that we can use the word chaos to describe the creation and annihilation events occurring continually among the particles rests on the existence of laws of probability. At best the probability, never the certainty, of these endless changes in the particle world can be known.

Are the laws of probability themselves derivable from conservation laws? The answer to this question is not yet known, but the trend of recent history is enough to make this author and many other physicists willing to bet on the affirmative. It appears possible, at least, that the conservation laws may not only be the most fundamental laws, but may be *all* the laws. They may be sufficient to characterize the elementary-particle world completely, specifying not only which events may occur and which are forbidden, but giving also the relative probabilities of those events which do occur.

We have so far emphasized that a conservation law is less restrictive than an explicit law of change, or law of permission. However, there are a number of different conservation laws and, taken all together, they may be very strongly restrictive, far more so than any one taken alone. In the ideal case, they may leave open only one possibility. The laws of prohibition, all taken together, then imply a unique law of permission. The most beautiful example of this kind of power of conservation laws concerns the nature of the photon. From conservation principles alone, it has been possible to show that the photon must be a massless particle of unit spin and no charge, emitted and absorbed by charged particles in a particular characteristic way. This truly amazing result has been expressed vividly by J. J. Sakurai who wrote recently, "The Creator was supremely imaginative when he declared, 'Let there be light.'"* In the world of human law, a man so hemmed in by restrictions that there is only one course of action open to him is

---

* *Annals of Physics*, Volume 11, page 5 (1960).

not very happy. In the world of natural law it is remarkable and satisfying to learn that a few simple statements about constant properties in nature can have locked within them such latent power that they determine uniquely the nature of light and its interaction with matter.

There are conservation laws and conservation laws. That is, some things in nature are constant, but others are even more constant. To convert this jargon into sense, some quantities in nature seem to be absolutely conserved, remaining unchanged in all events whatever; other quantities seem to be conserved in some kinds of processes and not in others. The rules governing the latter are still called conservation laws, but nature is permitted to violate them under certain circumstances. We shall postpone the discussion of these not-quite-conservation laws to Chapter Eight, and consider here only seven of the recognized absolute conservation laws. (There are two more absolute conservation laws of a more special kind, and they are also postponed to Chapter Eight.)

We begin by listing by name the seven quantities that are conserved:

1. Energy (including mass)
2. Momentum
3. Angular momentum, including spin
4. Charge
5. Electron-family number
6. Muon-family number
7. Baryon-family number.

There are two different kinds of quantities here, which can be called properties of motion and intrinsic properties, but the two are not clearly separated. The intrinsic particle properties that enter into the conservation laws are mass, spin, charge, and the several "family numbers." The properties of motion are kinetic energy, momentum, and angular momentum, the last frequently being called orbital angular momentum to avoid possible confusion with intrinsic spin, which is a form of angular momentum. In the laws of energy conservation and angular-momentum conservation, the intrinsic properties and properties of motion become mixed.

The interactions and transformations of the elementary particles serve admirably to illustrate the conservation laws and we shall focus attention on the particles for illustrative purposes. It is through studies of the particles that all of these conservation laws have been verified, although the first four were already known in the mac- roscopic world. The particles provide the best possible testing ground for conservation laws, for any law satisfied by small num- bers of particles is necessarily satisfied for all larger collections of particles, including the macroscopic objects of our everyday world. Whether the extrapolation of the submicroscopic conservation laws on into the cosmological domain is justified is uncertain, since gravity, whose effects in the particle world appear to be entirely negligible, becomes of dominant importance in the astronomical realm.

Various intrinsic properties of the particles were discussed in Chapter One, and we shall examine first the conservation laws that have to do with the intrinsic properties.

We learned in Chapter One that every particle carries the same electric charge as the electron (defined to be negative), or the equal and opposite charge of the proton (positive), or is neutral. The charge is a measure of the strength of electric force which the particle can exert and, correspondingly, a measure of the strength of electric force which the particle experiences. A neutral particle, of course, neither exerts nor responds to an electric force. A charged particle does both.

Using the proton charge as a unit, every particle's charge can be labeled $+1$, -1, or 0. The law of charge conservation requires that the total charge remain unchanged during every process of interaction or transformation. For any event involving particles, then, the total charge before the event must add up to the same value as the total charge after it. In the decay of a lambda into a neutron and a pion,

$$\Lambda^0 \rightarrow n + \pi^0,$$

the charge is zero both before and after. In the positive pion decay,

$$\pi^+ \rightarrow \mu^+ + \nu_\mu,$$

the products are a positive muon and a neutral neutrino. A possible high-energy nuclear collision might proceed as follows:

$$p + p \rightarrow n + \Lambda^0 + K^+ + \pi^+.$$

Neither positively charged proton survives the collision, but the net charge +2 appears on the particles created.

Notice that the law of charge conservation provides a partial explanation for the fact that particle charges come in only one size. If the charge on a pion were, say, 0.73 electron charges, it would be quite difficult to balance the books in transformation processes and maintain charge conservation. Actually, according to the present picture of elementary processes, the charge is conserved not only from "before" to "after," but at every intermediate stage of the process. One can visualize a single charge as an indivisible unit which, like a baton in a relay race, can be handed off from one particle to another, but never dropped or divided.

Perhaps the most salutary effect of the law of charge conservation in human affairs is the stabilization of the electron. The electron is the lightest charged particle and, for this reason alone, it cannot decay. The only lighter particles, the photon and neutrinos (and graviton) are neutral, and a decay of the electron would therefore necessarily violate the law of charge conservation. The stability of the electron is one of the simplest, yet one of the most stringent tests of the law of charge conservation. Nothing else prevents electron decay. If the law were almost, but not quite, valid, the electron should have a finite lifetime. A recent experiment places the electron lifetime beyond 10^{19} years; this means that charge conservation must be regarded as at least a very good approximation to an absolute law.

Unlike the other four laws, which were already known in the macroscopic world, the laws of family-number conservation were discovered through studies of particle transformation. We can best explain their meaning through examples. Recall that the proton and all heavier particles are called baryons, that is, they belong to the baryon family. In the decay of the unstable Λ particle,

$$\Lambda^0 \rightarrow p + \pi^-,$$

one baryon, the Λ, disappears, but another, the proton, appears. Similarly, in the decay of the Σ^0,

$$\Sigma^0 \rightarrow \Lambda^0 + \gamma,$$

the number of baryons is conserved. Notice that, in one of these examples, a pion is created; in the other, a photon. Pions and photons belong to none of the special family groups and can come and go in any number. In a typical proton-proton collision the number of baryons (2) remains unchanged, as in the example,

$$p + p \rightarrow p + \Sigma^+ + K^0.$$

These and numerous other examples have made it appear that the number of baryons remains forever constant—in every single event, and therefore, of course, in any larger structure.

Each of the Ω, Ξ, Σ, and Λ particles, and the neutron, undergoes spontaneous decay into a lighter baryon. But the lightest baryon, the proton, has nowhere to go. The law of baryon conservation stabilizes the proton and makes possible the structure of nuclei and atoms and, therefore, of our world. From the particle physicist's point of view, this is a truly miraculous phenomenon, for the proton stands perched at a mass nearly 2,000 times the electron mass, having an intrinsic energy of about one billion electron volts, while beneath it lie the lighter unstable kaon, pion, and muon. Only the law of baryon conservation holds this enormous energy locked within the proton and makes it a suitable building block for the universe. The proton appears to be absolutely stable. If it is unstable it has, according to a recent experimental result, a half life greater than 7×10^{27} years, or about a billion billion times the age of the earth.

Our statement of the law of baryon conservation needs some amplification, for we have not yet taken into account antibaryons. A typical antiproton-production event at the Berkeley Bevatron might go as follows:

$$p + p \rightarrow p + p + p + \bar{p}.$$

(The bar over the letter designates the antiparticle. Since the antiproton has negative charge, the total charge of plus 2 is conserved.) It appears that we have transformed two baryons into four. Similarly, in the antiproton annihilation event,

$$p + \bar{p} \rightarrow \pi^+ + \pi^- + \pi^0,$$

two baryons have apparently vanished. The obvious way to patch up the law of baryon conservation is to assign to the antiparticles baryon number -1, and to the particles baryon number $+1$. Then the law would read: In every event the total number of baryons *minus* the total number of antibaryons is conserved; or, equivalently, the total baryon number remains unchanged.

The cynic might say that with so many arbitrary definitions— which particles should be called baryons and which not, and the use of negative baryon numbers—it is no wonder that a conservation law can be constructed. To this objection, two excellent answers can be given. The first is that it is not so easy to find an absolute conservation law. To find any quantity absolutely conserved in nature is so important that it easily justifies a few arbitrary definitions. The arbitrariness at this stage of history only reflects our lack of any deep understanding of the reason for baryon conservation, but it does not detract from the obvious significance of baryon conservation as a law of nature. The other answer, based on the mathematics of the quantum theory, is that the use of negative baryon number for antiparticles is perfectly natural, in fact, is demanded by the theory. This comes about because the description of the appearance of an antiparticle is "equivalent" (in a mathematical sense we cannot delve into*) to the description of the disappearance of a particle; and conversely antiparticle annihilation is "equivalent" to particle creation.

The "electron family" contains only the electron and its neutrino, the "muon family" only the muon and its neutrino. For each of these small groups, there is a conservation of family members exactly like the conservation of baryons. The antiparticles must be considered negative members of the families, the particles positive members. These light-particle conservation laws are not nearly as well tested as the other absolute conservation laws because of the difficulties of studying neutrinos, but there are no known exceptions to them.

The beta decay of the neutron,

$$n \rightarrow p + e^- + \overline{\nu_e},$$

illustrates nicely the conservation laws we have discussed. Initially, the single neutron has charge zero, baryon number 1, and electron-family number zero. The oppositely charged proton and electron preserve zero charge; the single proton preserves the baryon number; and the electron with its antineutrino ($\overline{\nu_e}$) together preserve zero electron-family number. In the pion decay processes,

$$\pi^+ \rightarrow \mu^+ + \nu_\mu \quad \text{and} \quad \pi^- \rightarrow \mu^- + \overline{\nu_\mu},$$

---

* See page 200 where antiparticles are described as "particles moving backwards in time."

muon-family conservation demands that a neutrino accompany the μ^+ antimuon, and an antineutrino accompany the μ^- muon. The muon, in turn, decays into three particles, for example,

$$\mu^- \rightarrow e^- + \nu_\mu + \overline{\nu_e},$$

which conserves the members of the muon family and of the electron family.

The general rule enunciated earlier in this chapter was that whatever *can* happen without violating a conservation law *does* happen. Until 1962, there was a notable exception to this rule; its resolution has beautifully strengthened the idea that conservation laws play a central role in the world of elementary particles. The decay of a muon into an electron and a photon,

$$\mu^- \rightarrow e^- + \gamma,$$

has never been seen, a circumstance which had come to be known as the μ-e-γ puzzle. Before the discovery of the muon's neutrino it was believed that electron, muon, and one neutrino formed a single family (called the lepton family) with a single family-conservation law. If this were the case, no conservation law prohibited the decay of muon into electron and photon, since the lost muon was replaced with an electron, and charge and all other quantities were conserved as well. According to the classical view of physical law, the absence of this process should have caused no concern. There was, after all, no law of permission which said that it should occur. There was only the double negative: No conservation law was known to prohibit the decay.

However, the view of the fundamental role of conservation laws in nature as the only inhibition on physical processes had become so ingrained in the thinking of physicists that the absence of this particular decay mode of the muon was regarded as a significant mystery. It was largely this mystery that stimulated the search for a second neutrino belonging exclusively to the muon. The discovery of the muon's neutrino established as a near certainty that the electron and muon belong to two different small families which are separately conserved. With the electron and muon governed by two separate laws of conservation, the prohibition of the μ-e-γ decay became immediately explicable, and the faith that what can happen does happen was further bolstered.

We turn now to the conservation laws which involve properties of motion (the first three in the list on page 85).

In the world of particles there are only two kinds of energy: energy of motion, or kinetic energy, and energy of being, which is equivalent to mass. Whenever particles are created or annihilated (except the massless particles) energy is transformed from one form to the other, but the total energy in every process always remains conserved. The simplest consequence of energy conservation for the spontaneous decay of unstable particles is that the total mass of the products must be less than the mass of the parent. For each of the following decay processes the masses on the right add up to less than the mass on the left:

$$K^+ \rightarrow \pi^+ + \pi^+ + \pi^-,$$
$$\Xi^- \rightarrow \Lambda^0 + \pi^-,$$
$$\mu^+ \rightarrow e^+ + \nu_e + \overline{\nu_\mu}.$$

In particular, then, a massless particle cannot decay, and energy conservation prohibits every other "uphill" decay in which the products are heavier than the parent. An unstable particle at rest has only its energy of being, no energy of motion. The difference between this parent mass and the mass of the product particles is transformed into kinetic energy which the product particles carry away as they rapidly leave the scene.

One might suppose that if the parent particle is moving when it decays it has some energy of motion of its own which might be transformed to mass. The conservation of momentum prohibits this. The extra energy of motion is in fact "unavailable" for conversion into mass. If a particle loses energy, it also loses momentum. Momentum conservation therefore prohibits the conversion of all of the energy into mass. It turns out that momentum and energy conservation taken together forbid uphill decays into heavier particles no matter how fast the initial particle might be moving.

If two particles collide, on the other hand, some—but not all—of their energy of motion is available to create mass. It is in this way that the various unstable particles are manufactured in the laboratory. In an actual typical collision in the vicinity of an accelerator, one of the two particles, the projectile, is moving rapidly, and the other, the target, is at rest. Under these conditions, the requirement that the final particles should have as much momentum as the initial projectile severely restricts the amount of energy that can be converted into mass. This is too bad, for the projectile has been given a great energy at a great expense. To make a proton-antiproton pair, for example, by the projectile-hitting-fixed-target method, the projectile must have a kinetic energy of 6 Bev (billion electron volts), of which only 2 Bev goes into making the mass. The 6 Bev Berkeley Bevatron was designed with this fact in mind in order to be able to make antiprotons and antineutrons. Typical processes for protons striking protons are:

$$p + p \rightarrow p + p + p + \bar{p},$$
$$p + p \rightarrow p + p + n + \bar{n}.$$

The unfortunate waste of 4 Bev in these processes could be avoided if the target proton were not quiescent, but flew at the projectile with equal and opposite speed. It is hard enough to produce one high-energy beam, and far more difficult to produce two at once. Nevertheless, the gain in available energy makes it worth the trouble, and a technique for producing "clashing beams" is now employed at Stanford University, where oppositely directed beams of electrons collide. The device is sometimes called by physicists the synchroclash.

Momentum is purely a property of motion—that is, if there is no motion, there is no momentum. It is somewhat trickier than energy, for momentum is what is called a vector quantity. It has direction as well as magnitude. Vectors are actually familiar in everyday life, whether or not we know them by that name. The velocity of an automobile is a vector, with a magnitude (50 miles per hour, for example) and a direction (northbound, for example). Force is a vector, a push or pull of some strength in some direction. Mass, on the other hand, is not a vector. It points in no particular direction. Energy also has no direction. The momentum of a rolling freight car, however, is directed along the tracks, and the momentum of an elementary particle is directed along its course through space.

In order to appreciate the law of momentum conservation, one must know how to add vectors. Two men pushing on a stalled car are engaged in adding vectors. If they push with equal strength *and* in the same direction, the total force exerted is twice the force each one exerts and, of course, in the direction they are pushing [Figure 4.1(a)]. If they push with equal strength but at opposite ends of the car, their effort comes to naught, for the sum of two vector quantities which are equal in strength but opposite in direction is

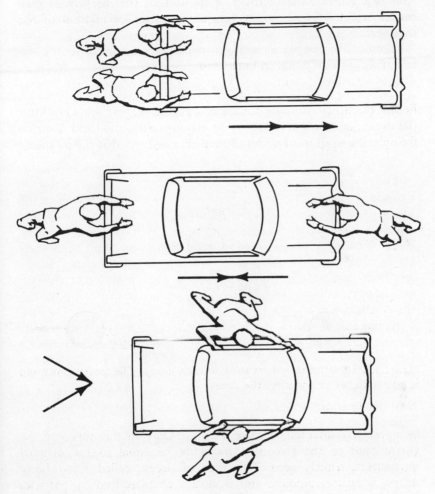

Figure 4.1. The addition of vectors. The forces exerted by two men pushing equally hard may be "added," that is, combined, to give any total from zero up to twice the force of each.

zero [Figure 4.1(b)]. If they get on opposite sides of the car and push partly inward, partly forward, the net force exerted will be forward, but less than twice the force of each [Figure 4.1(c)]. Depending on their degree of co-operation, the two men may achieve a strength of force from zero up to twice the force each can exert.

This is a general characteristic of the sum of two vectors. It may have a wide range of values depending on the orientation of the two vectors.

Consider the law of momentum conservation applied to the decay of a kaon into muon and neutrino,

$$K^+ \rightarrow \mu^+ + \nu_\mu.$$

Before the decay, suppose the kaon is at rest [Figure 4.2(a)]. After the decay, momentum conservation requires that muon and neutrino fly off with equal magnitudes of momenta *and* and that the momenta

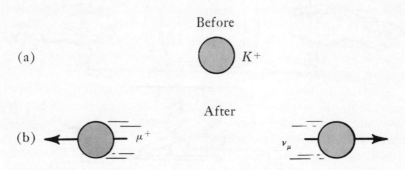

Before

(a) K^+

After

(b) μ^+ ν_μ

Figure 4.2. Momentum conservation in kaon decay. The total momentum is zero both before and after the decay.

be oppositely directed [Figure 4.2(b)]. Only in this way can the vector sum of the two final momenta be equal to the original momentum, namely zero. This type of decay, called a two-body decay, is rather common, and is always characterized by particles emerging in exactly opposite directions.

In a three-body decay, the emerging particles have more freedom. Figure 1.8, for example, shows the decay of a kaon into three pions with the tracks pointing in three different directions. Recalling the analogy between momentum and force, one can visualize a situation in which three different forces are acting and producing no net effect—two fighters and a referee all pushing in different directions in a clinch. Similarly, the momentum vectors must adjust themselves to produce no net effect; that is, they must add up to give zero. Momentum conservation on a grander scale is shown in Figure 4.3, where eight particles emerge from a single event.

One vital prohibition of the law of momentum conservation is that against one-body decays. Consider, for example, this possibility,

$$K^+ \rightarrow \pi^+,$$

the transformation of kaon to pion. It satisfies the laws of charge and family-number conservation. It is consistent with energy conservation, for it is downhill in mass, and it also satisfies spin conservation. But the kaon-pion mass difference must get converted to energy of motion, so that if the kaon was at rest, the pion will fly away. In whatever direction it moves, it has some momentum and therefore violates momentum conservation, since the kaon had none. On the other hand, if we enforce the law of momentum conservation, and keep the pion at rest, we shall have violated energy conservation, for in this case the extra energy arising from the mass difference will be unaccounted for.

Angular momentum, a measure of the strength of rotational motion, has been a key concept in physics since the time of Kepler. Actually, Kepler did not recognize it as such, but the second of his three laws of planetary motion—the so-called law of areas—is equivalent to a law of conservation of angular momentum. According to this law, an imaginary straight line drawn from the earth to the sun sweeps out area in space at a constant rate. During a single day this line sweeps across a thin triangular region with apex at the sun and base along the earth's orbit. The area of this triangle is the same for every day of the year. So, when the earth is closer to the sun, it must move faster in order to define a triangle with the same area. It speeds up just enough, in fact, to maintain a constant value of its angular momentum, and the law of areas can be derived as a simple consequence of the law of conservation of angular momentum (this was first done by Newton).

The earth also serves to illustrate approximately the two kinds of angular momentum which enter into the conservation law—orbital and spin. The earth possesses angular momentum because of its orbital motion round the sun and because of its daily (spin) rotation about its own axis. For an elementary particle, the notion of spin is about the same as for the earth—rotational motion about an axis.

If a photographer in space took a time exposure of the earth and

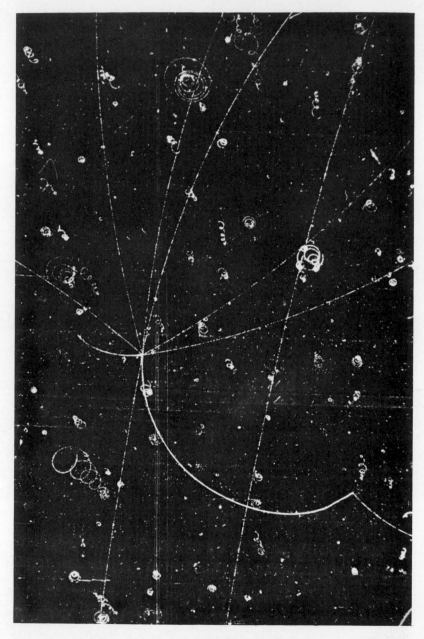

Figure 4.3. For descriptive legend see page 97.

sun, his photograph would contain a short blur for the sun and a longer blur for the earth. He would notice that the blurs were not directed toward each other, and from this fact alone could conclude that earth and sun possess relative angular momentum. He would not need to know whether the earth swings around the sun or whether it proceeds into interstellar space. The key fact defining orbital angular momentum is some transverse motion of two objects. Any two moving objects, not aimed directly at each other, possess relative angular momentum. Two trains passing on the great plains have relative angular momentum, even though each is proceeding straight as an arrow. But if, through some mischance, both were on the same track on a collision course, they would have zero angular momentum. In particle collisions and decays, orbital angular momentum is usually of this trains-in-the-plains type, not involving actual orbiting of one particle round another. Figure 4.4 illustrates several examples of motion with angular momentum.

Angular momentum is a vector quantity. Its direction is taken to be the axis of rotation. The axis is well defined for spin, but what about orbital motion? For the passing trains, imagine again the blurred photograph indicating their direction of motion. Then ask: What would the axis be if the trains rotated about each other, instead of proceeding onward? The answer is a vertical axis; the angular momentum is directed upward. One more fact about orbital angular momentum needs to be known. Unlike spin, which comes in units of $\frac{1}{2}\hbar$, it comes only in units of $\hbar$.

The spinless pion decays into muon and neutrino, each with spin $\frac{1}{2}$. In Figure 4.5 we use artistic license and represent the particles by little spheres with arrows to indicate their direction of spin. Muon and neutrino spin oppositely in order to preserve the

---

Figure 4.3. Momentum conservation in an antiproton annihilation event. An antiproton entering from the bottom collides with a proton in the bubble chamber. Eight pions, four negative and four positive, spray off from the annihilation event in all directions. The momentum of each can be measured from the curvature of the track; the eight momenta added together as vectors are just equal to the momentum of the single incoming antiproton. (The kink in the track at the lower right is a pion decay, $\pi^+ \rightarrow \mu^+ + \nu_\mu$. In what general direction did the unseen neutrino fly off?)

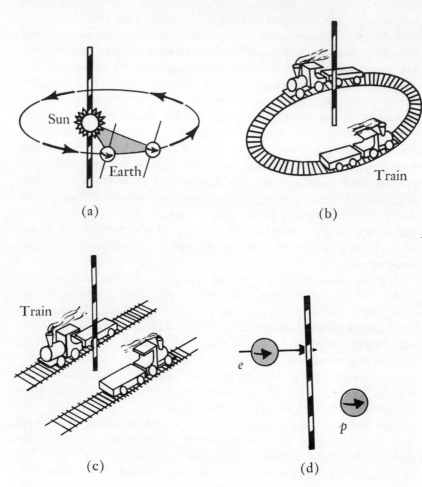

Figure 4.4. Examples of motion with angular momentum. (a) The earth possesses spin angular momentum about its axis as well as orbital angular momentum about an axis designated by the giant barber pole. The constancy of the earth's orbital angular momentum means that the shaded area swept out in one day is the same for every day of the year. (b) Trains on a circular track possess angular momentum about a vertical axis. (c) Even on straight tracks, a similar relative motion of trains represents angular momentum. (d) An electron flies past a proton. Both particles possess spin angular momentum and, because they are not on a collision course, they also have orbital angular momentum.

total zero angular momentum. In this case, no orbital angular momentum is involved.

Another two-body decay, that of the Λ, illustrates the coupling of spin and orbital motion. The Λ, supposed initially at rest [Figure 4.6(a)], has spin ½. One of its possible decay modes is

$$\Lambda^0 \rightarrow p + \pi^-.$$

This may proceed in two ways. The proton and pion may move apart with no orbital angular momentum, the proton spin directed upward to match the initial Λ spin [Figure 4.6(b)]; or the proton spin may be flipped to point downward while proton and pion

Before (no spin)

π^+

After (cancelling spin)

μ^+ ν_μ

Figure 4.5. Angular-momentum conservation in pion decay. The total angular momentum is zero before and after the decay.

separate with one unit of orbital angular momentum, directed upward [Figure 4.6(c)]. In the first case,

original spin ½ (up) → final spin ½ (up).

In the second case,

original spin ½ (up) → final spin ½ (down) + orbital angular
momentum 1 (up).

Beta decay, the earliest known particle decay process, serves nicely to illustrate all of the absolute conservation laws discussed. The beta decay of the neutron, indicated symbolically by

$$n \rightarrow p + e^- + \overline{\nu_e},$$

is pictured in Figure 4.7. Consider now the conservation laws applied to this decay.

Energy. Reference to Table 1 shows that the sum of the masses of the proton (1836.12), the electron (1.0), and the electron's

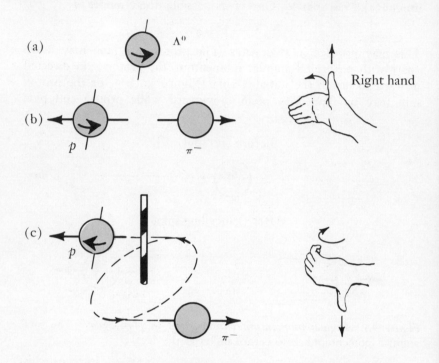

Figure 4.6. Angular-momentum conservation in lambda decay. The direction of angular momentum is defined by the right-hand rule. If the curved fingers of the right hand point in the direction of rotational motion, the right thumb defines the direction assigned to the angular momentum. Thus the particle spin is up in diagrams (a) and (b) and down in diagram (c); the orbital angular momentum is up in diagram (c).

neutrino (0), add up to less than the neutron mass (1838.65). The decay is therefore an allowed downhill decay, the slight excess mass going into kinetic energy of the products.

Momentum. The three particles must fan off in different directions with the available excess energy so distributed among them that the sum of the three momentum vectors is zero.

Angular momentum. One possibility, illustrated in Figure 4.7, is that the departing electron and proton have opposite cancelling spins, while the neutrino spins in the same direction as the original neutron to conserve the angular momentum.

Charge. The final charge (1 positive, 1 negative, 1 neutral) is zero, the same as the initial neutron charge.

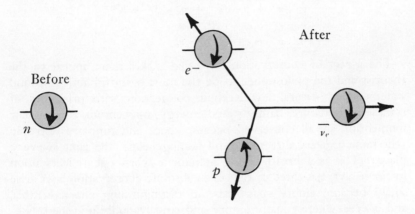

Figure 4.7. Beta decay of the neutron, $n \rightarrow p + e^- + \overline{\nu}_e$.

Electron-family number. The neutron has zero electron-family number. In the decay, one electron and one antineutrino ($\overline{\nu}_e$) are created to preserve zero electron-family number.

Muon-family number. No members of the muon family are created or destroyed.

Baryon number. The proton is the single baryon among the final three particles, matching the single original baryon.

Now we propose an exercise for the reader. Below are listed a few decays and transformations which do *not* occur in nature. If only one particle stands on the left, a decay process is understood. If two particles stand on the left, a collision process is understood. At least one conservation law prohibits each of these processes. Find at least one conservation law violated by each process. Several violate more than one law and one of those listed violates five of the seven conservation laws. (Answers are given on page 111.)

a. $\mu^+ \rightarrow \pi^+ + \nu_\mu$

b. $e^- \rightarrow \nu_e + \gamma$

c. $p + p \rightarrow p + \Lambda^0 + \Sigma^+$

d. $\mu^+ \rightarrow \Lambda^0$

e. $n \rightarrow \mu^+ + e^- + \gamma$

f. $\Lambda^0 \rightarrow p + e^-$

g. $\pi^- + p \rightarrow \pi^- + n + \Lambda^0 + K^+$

h. $e^+ + e^- \rightarrow \mu^+ + \pi^-$

i. $\mu^- \rightarrow e^- + e^+ + \nu_\mu$

The aspect of conservation laws that makes them appear to the theorist and the philosopher to be the most beautiful and profound statements of natural law is their connection with principles of symmetry in nature. Baldly stated, energy, momentum, and angular momentum are all conserved because space and time are isotropic (the same in every direction) and homogeneous (the same at every place). This is a breath-taking statement when one reflects upon it, for it says that three of the seven absolute conservation laws arise solely because empty space has no distinguishing characteristics, and is everywhere equally empty and equally undistinguished. (Because of the relativistic link between space and time, we really mean space-time.) It seems, in the truest sense, that we are getting something from nothing.

Yet there can be no doubt about the connection between the properties of empty space and the fundamental conservation laws which govern elementary-particle behavior. This connection raises philosophical questions which we will mention but not pursue at any length. On the one hand, it may be interpreted to mean that conservation laws, being based on the most elementary and intuitive ideas, are the most profound statements of natural law. On the other hand, one may argue, as Bertrand Russell* has done, that it only demonstrates the hollowness of conservation laws ("truisms," according to Russell), energy, momentum, and angular momentum all being defined in just such a way that they must be conserved. Now, in fact, it is not inconsistent to hold both views at once. If

---

* Bertrand Russell, *The ABC of Relativity* (New York: New American Library, 1959).

the aim of science is the self-consistent description of natural phenomena based upon the simplest set of basic assumptions, what could be more satisfying than to have basic assumptions so completely elementary and self-evident (the uniformity of space-time) that the laws derived from them can be called truisms? Since the scientist generally is inclined to call most profound that which is most simple and most general, he is not above calling a truism profound. Speaking more pragmatically, we must recognize the discovery of *anything* that is absolutely conserved as something of an achievement, regardless of the arbitrariness of definition involved. Looking at those conservation laws whose basis we do not understand (the three family-number-conservation laws) also brings home the fact that it is easier to call a conservation law a truism after it is understood than before. It seems quite likely that we shall gain a deeper understanding of nature and of natural laws before the conservation of baryon number appears to anyone to be a self-evident truth.

Before trying to clarify through simple examples the connection between conservation laws and the uniformity of space, we consider the question, "What is symmetry?" In most general terms, symmetry means that when one thing (A) is changed in some particular way, something else (B) remains unchanged. A symmetrical face is one whose appearance (B) would remain the same if its two sides (A) were interchanged. If a square figure (A) is rotated through 90 degrees, its appearance (B) is not changed. Among plane figures, the circle is the most symmetrical, for if it is rotated about its center through any angle whatever, it remains indistinguishable from the original circle—or, in the language of modern physics, its form remains invariant. In the language of ancient Greece, the circle is the most perfect and most beautiful of plane figures.

Aristotle regarded the motion of the celestial bodies as necessarily circular because of the perfection (the symmetry) of the circle. Now, from a still deeper symmetry of space-time, we can derive the ellipses of Kepler. Modern science, which could begin only after breaking loose from the centuries-old hold of Aristotelian physics, now finds itself with an unexpected Aristotelian flavor, coming both from the increasingly dominant role of symmetry principles and from the increasingly geometrical basis of physics.

We are accustomed to think of symmetry in spatial terms. The symmetry of the circle, the square, and the face are associated with rotations or inversions in space. Symmetry in time is an obvious extension of spatial symmetry; the fact that nature's laws appear to remain unchanged as time passes is a fundamental symmetry of nature. However, there exist some subtler symmetries, and it is reasonable to guess that the understanding of baryon conservation, for example, will come through the discovery of new symmetries not directly connected with space and time.

In the symmetry of interest to the scientist, the unchanging thing—the invariant element—is the form of natural laws. The thing changed may be orientation in space, or position in space or time, or some more abstract change (not necessarily realizable in practice) such as the interchange of two particles. The inversion of space and the reversal of the direction of flow of time are other examples of changes not realizable in practice, but nonetheless of interest for the symmetries of natural law. These latter two will be discussed in Chapter Eight.

If scientists in Chicago, New York, and Geneva perform the same experiment and get the same answer (within experimental error) they are demonstrating one of the symmetries of nature, the homogeneity of space. If the experiment is repeated later with the same result, no one is surprised, for we have come to accept the homogeneity of time. The laws of nature are the same, so far as we know, at all points in space, and for all times. This invariance is important and is related to the laws of conservation of energy and momentum, but ordinary experience conditions us to expect such invariance so that it seems at first to be trivial or self-evident. It might seem hard to visualize any science at all if natural law changed from place to place and time to time, but, in fact, quantitative science would be perfectly possible without the homogeneity of space-time. Imagine yourself, for example, on a merry-go-round that speeded up and slowed down according to a regular schedule. If you carried out experiments to deduce the laws of mechanics and had no way of knowing that you were on a rotating system, you would conclude that falling balls were governed by laws which varied with time and with position (distance from central axis), but you would be quite able to work out the laws in detail and predict accurately the results of future experiments, provided you knew where and when the experiment was to be carried out. Thanks to the actual homogeneity of space and time, the results of future experiments can in fact be predicted without any knowledge of the where or when.

A slightly less obvious kind of invariance, although one also familiar from ordinary experience, is the invariance of the laws of nature for systems in uniform motion. Passengers on an ideally smooth train or in an ideally smooth elevator are unaware of motion. If the laws of mechanics were significantly altered, the riders would be aware of it through unusual bodily sensations. Such a qualitative guide is, of course, not entirely reliable, but careful experiments performed inside the ideal uniformly moving train would reveal the same laws of nature revealed by corresponding experiments conducted in a stationary laboratory. This particular invariance underlies the theory of relativity, and is a manifestation of the isotropy of four-dimensional space-time, a point we can regrettably not discuss in detail. What, to our limited three-dimensional vision, appears to be uniform motion is, to a more enlightened brain capable of encompassing four dimensions, merely a rotation. Instead of turning, say, from north to east, the experimenter who climbs aboard the train is, from the more general view, turning from space partly toward the time direction. According to relativity, which joins space and time together in a four-dimensional space-time, the laws of nature should no more be changed by "turning" experimental apparatus toward the time direction (that is, loading it aboard the train) than by turning it through 90 degrees in the laboratory.

The chain of connection we have been discussing is: Symmetry → invariance → conservation. The symmetry of space and time, or possibly some subtler symmetry of nature, implies the invariance of physical laws under certain changes associated with the symmetry. In the simplest case, for example, the symmetry of space which we call its homogeneity implies the invariance of experimental results when the apparatus is moved from one place to another. This invariance, in turn, implies the existence of certain conservation laws. The relation between conservation laws and symmetry principles is what we now wish to illuminate through two examples. Unfortunately, an adequate discussion of this important connection requires the use of mathematics beyond the scope of this book.

Suppose we imagine a single isolated hydrogen atom alone and at rest in empty space. If we could draw up a chair and observe it without influencing it, what should we expect to see? (For this discussion, we ignore quantum mechanics and the wave nature of particles, pretending that electron and proton may be separately seen as particles, and be uninfluenced by the observer. The reader will have to accept the fact that these false assumptions are permissible and irrelevant for the present discussion.) We should see an electron in rapid motion circling about a proton, and the proton itself moving more slowly in a smaller circle. Were we to back off until the whole atom could only be discerned as a single spot, that spot, if initially motionless, would remain at rest forever. We now must ask whether this circumstance is significant or insignificant, important or dull. It certainly does not seem surprising. Why should the atom move, we may ask. It is isolated from the rest of the universe, no forces act upon it from outside, therefore there is nothing to set it into motion. If we leave a book on a table and come back later, we expect to find it there. Everyday experience conditions us to expect that an object on which no external forces act will not spontaneously set itself into motion. There is no more reason for the atom to begin to move than for the book to migrate across the table and fly into a corner. The trouble with this argument is that it makes use of the common sense of ordinary experience, without offering any explanation for the ordinary experience.

If we put aside "common sense" and ask what the atom might do, it is by no means obvious that it should remain at rest. In spite of the fact that no external forces are acting, strong internal forces are at work. The proton exerts a force on the electron which constantly alters its motion; the electron, in turn, exerts a force on the proton. Both atomic constituents are experiencing force. Why should these forces not combine to set the atom as a whole into motion? Having put the question in this way, we may consider the book on the table again. It consists of countless billions of atoms, each one exerting forces on its neighboring atoms. Through what miracle do these forces so precisely cancel out that no net force acts upon the book as a whole and it remains quiescent on the table?

The classical approach to this problem is to look for a positive, or permissive, law, a law which tells what *does* happen. Newton first enunciated this law which (except for some modification made necessary by the theory of relativity) has withstood the test of time to the present day. It is called Newton's third law, and says that all forces in nature occur in equal and opposite balanced pairs. The proton's force on the electron is exactly equal and opposite to the electron's force on the proton. The sum of these two forces (the *vector* sum) is zero, so that there is no tendency for the structure as a whole to move in any direction. The balancing of forces, moreover, can be related to a balancing of momenta. By making use of Newton's second law,* which relates the motion to the force, one can discover that, in a hydrogen atom initially at rest, the balanced forces will cause the momenta of electron and proton to be equal and opposite. At a given instant, the two particles are moving in opposite directions. The heavier proton moves more slowly, but has the same momentum as the electron. As the electron swings to a new direction and a new speed in its track, the proton swings too in just such a way that its momentum remains equal and opposite to that of the electron. In spite of the continuously changing momenta of the two particles, the total momentum of the atom remains zero; the atom does not move. In this way—by "discovering" and applying two laws, Newton's second and third laws of motion—one derives the law of momentum conservation and finds an explanation of the fact that an isolated atom does not move.

Without difficulty, the same arguments may be applied to the book on the table. Since all forces come in equal and opposite pairs, the forces between every pair of atoms cancel, so that the total force is zero, no matter how many billions of billions of atoms and individual forces there might be.

It is worth reviewing the steps in the argument above. Two laws of permission were discovered, telling what does happen. One law relates the motion to the force; the other says that the forces between pairs of particles are always equal and opposite. From these laws, the conservation of momentum was derived as an interesting consequence, and this conservation law in turn explained the fact that an isolated atom at rest remains at rest.

The modern approach to the problem starts in quite a different way, by seeking a law of prohibition, a principle explaining why the atom does *not* move. This principle is the invariance of laws of nature to a change of position. Recall the chain of key ideas

---

* Newton's second law, usually written $F = ma$, says that the acceleration a experienced by a particle multiplied by its mass m is equal to the force F acting upon it. The law may also be stated in this way: The rate at which the momentum of a particle is changing is equal to the force applied.

referred to on page 105: symmetry → invariance → conservation. In the example of the isolated hydrogen atom, the symmetry of interest is the homogeneity of space. Founded upon this symmetry is the invariance principle just cited. Finally, the conservation law resting on this invariance principle is the conservation of momentum.

In order to clarify, through the example of the hydrogen atom, the connecting links between the assumed homogeneity of space and the conservation of momentum, we must begin with an exact statement of the invariance principle as applied to our isolated atom. The principle is this: No aspect of the motion of an isolated atom depends upon the location of the center of mass of the atom. The center of mass of any object is the average position of all of the mass in the object. In a hydrogen atom, the center of mass is a point in space between the electron and the proton, close to the more massive proton.

Let us visualize our hydrogen atom isolated in empty space with its center of mass at rest. Suppose now that its center of mass starts to move. In which direction should it move? We confront at once the question of the homogeneity of space. Investing our atom with human qualities for a moment, we can say that it has no basis upon which to "decide" how to move. To the atom surveying the possibilities, every direction is precisely as good or bad as every other direction. It is therefore frustrated in its "desire" to move and simply remains at rest.

This anthropomorphic description of the situation can be replaced by sound mathematics. What the mathematics shows is that an acceleration of the center of mass—for example, changing from a state of rest to a state of motion—is not consistent with the assumption that the laws of motion of the atom are independent of the location of the center of mass. If the center of mass of the atom is initially at rest at point A and it then begins to move, it will later pass through another point B. At point A, the center of mass had no velocity. At point B it does have a velocity. Therefore, the state of motion of the atom depends on the location of the center of mass, contrary to the invariance principle. Only if the center of mass remains at rest can the atom satisfy the invariance principle.* The immobility of the center of mass requires, in turn, that the two particles composing the atom have equal and opposite momenta.

---

* If the center of mass of the atom had been moving initially, the invariance principle requires that it continue moving with constant velocity.

A continual balancing of the two momenta means that their sum, the total momentum, is a constant.

The argument thus proceeds directly from the symmetry principle to the conservation law without making use of Newton's laws of motion. That this is a deeper approach to conservation laws, as well as a more esthetically pleasing one, has been verified by history. Although Newton's laws of motion have been altered by relativity and by quantum mechanics, the direct connection between the symmetry of space and the conservation of momentum has been unaffected—or even strengthened—by these modern theories and momentum conservation remains one of the pillars of modern physics. We must recognize that a violation of the law of momentum conservation would imply an inhomogeneity of space; this is not an impossibility, but it would have far-reaching consequences for our view of the universe.

Returning finally to the book on the table, we want to emphasize that the quiescence of the undisturbed book—a macroscopic object—at least strongly suggests that momentum conservation must be a valid law in the microscopic world. Viewed microscopically, the book is a collection of an enormous number of atoms, each one in motion. That this continuous microscopic motion never makes itself felt as spontaneous bulk motion of the whole book is true only because of the conservation of momentum which requires that every time an atom changes its momentum (as it is constantly doing) one or more other atoms must undergo exactly compensating changes of their momentum.

Through similar examples it is possible to relate the law of conservation of angular momentum to the isotropy of space. A compass needle which is held pointing east and is then released will swing toward the north because of the action of the earth's magnetic field upon it. But if the same compass needle is taken to the depths of empty space, far removed from all external influences, and set to point in some direction, it will remain pointing in that direction. A swing in one direction or the other would imply a nonuniformity* of space. If the uniformity of space is adopted as a fundamental symmetry principle, it can be concluded that the

---

* Strictly, momentum conservation rests on the *homogeneity* of space (uniformity of place), and angular momentum conservation rests on the *isotropy* of space (uniformity of direction). The distinction is not important for our purposes, and it is satisfactory to think of space simply as everywhere the same, homogeneity and isotropy being summarized by the word uniformity.

total angular momentum of all the atomic constituents of the needle must be a constant. Otherwise, the internal motions within the needle could set the whole needle into spontaneous rotation and its motion would violate the symmetry principle.

Energy conservation, in a way that is not so easy to see, is related to the homogeneity of time. Thus all three conservation laws—of energy, momentum, and angular momentum—are "understood" in terms of the symmetry of space-time, and indeed the theory of relativity has shown that these three laws are all parts of a single general conservation law in the four-dimensional world.

Only one of the three conservation laws governing the intrinsic properties of the particles has so far been understood in terms of a symmetry principle. This is the law of charge conservation. (Recall, however, that the *quantization* of charge is not yet understood.) The symmetry principle underlying charge conservation is considerably more subtle than the space-time symmetry underlying the conservation laws of properties of motion. The modern version of this symmetry principle rests upon technical aspects of the theory of quantum mechanics (it may be based also on equally technical aspects of the theory of electromagnetism). Nevertheless, it is such a stunning victory for the power of a symmetry principle that we must try, however crudely, to indicate the modern view of this symmetry.

In the main, the classical theories of physics deal directly with quantities which are measurable, usually called observables. Force, mass, velocity, and almost all the other concepts described by the classical laws are themselves observables. The equations of quantum mechanics, however, contain quantities which are not themselves observables. From these quantities—one step removed from reality —the observables are derived. The "wave function" is one of the unobservable quantities; it determines the probability, say, that the electron is at any particular point in the hydrogen atom, but is itself not that probability nor any other measurable thing. Now enters the idea of symmetry. Any change that can be made in the unobservable quantity without resulting in a change of the observables ought to leave all the laws of nature unchanged. After careful scrutiny, this statement seems so obviously true that it is hard to understand how it could have any important consequences. Of course one ought to be able to do anything whatever to unobservable quantities so long as observables are not changed. But remember how important were the properties of empty space. Equally important are the properties of unobservables such as wave functions.

Space itself may be regarded as an unobservable. The uniformity of space means that it is impossible, by any experimental means, to ascertain one's absolute position in space. An experiment carried out at one place will yield results identical to the results of the same experiment carried out at another place. Any change in the unobservable space (for instance, moving the apparatus from one place to another) must leave unchanged the laws of nature and the observable results of experiment. As we have just seen, this symmetry principle or invariance requirement underlies the law of momentum conservation.

When an analogous symmetry principle is applied to the unobservable wave function of the electron a conservation law results, the conservation of charge. Expressed negatively, if charge were not conserved, the form of the equations of quantum mechanics would depend upon unobservable quantities, a situation at variance with our symmetry principle. The analogous statement for spatial homogeneity would be: If momentum were not conserved, the laws of mechanics would depend upon the absolute location in space and such dependence is at variance with the assumed symmetry of space.

Regrettably, we can not explain the law of charge conservation more fully without mathematics. It is expected, but not yet verified, that some undiscovered subtle symmetries of nature underlie the laws of electron-family conservation, muon-family conservation, and baryon conservation. The absolute prohibition of proton decay, which keeps its enormous intrinsic energy locked forever in the form of mass, can be no accident, but the reason still remains hidden.

Answers

The particle transformations listed on page 102 *violate* the following conservation laws:

a. Energy (an "uphill" decay); muon-family number (since μ^+ is an antiparticle).
b. Charge.
c. Angular momentum; baryon number.
d. Energy; momentum (a one-particle decay); charge; muon-

family number; baryon number.

e. Angular momentum; baryon number; muon-family number; electron-family number.

f. Angular momentum; electron-family number.

g. Angular momentum; baryon number.

h. Angular momentum; muon-family number.

i. Charge. (Why is angular momentum conservation satisfied?)

Chapter Five

Photons and Neutrinos

One of the massless particles, the photon, we see every day. The other known massless particles, the neutrinos, have been "seen" only by a handful of physicists, and then only with the help of some very elaborate equipment. The fourth massless particle, the graviton, still exists only in theory. It has never been observed, and there seems to be little hope that it will be detected in the near future.

The massless particles have a particular fascination of their own, and a particular importance; in this chapter we shall discuss those which are known, the photon and the neutrinos, adding a word at the end about why the graviton is hard to see.

For every particle with mass, the value of the mass and the value of the charge suffice to identify the particle unambiguously. "The negative particle with a mass of 9×10^{-28} gm" can indicate only one thing, the electron. The neutral particle with a mass of 1.7×10^{-24} gm can be only the neutron. If we say "the neutral particle with no mass" we might mean the photon, either of the neutrinos, or the graviton. Yet a glance at Table 1 will show differences among these particles. The photon has one unit of spin (intrinsic angular momentum), the neutrinos have one-half unit of spin, and the graviton has, theoretically, two units of spin. Also the neutrinos belong to the electron and muon families and the others do not. Even more marked are the differences in how these particles are created and absorbed, that is, how they interact with other particles.

The massless particles might be described as the "most wave-like" of particles, for they defy visualization as particles. Extrapolating our macroscopic idea of a particle downward to vanishing mass is no help, for in this way we only arrive at the conclusion: No mass, no particle. The trouble is that massless particles are "essentially" relativistic. They cannot be slowed down, for they

113

move always at the same fixed speed, the speed of light, and they cannot be localized. Our imagination is not equipped to deal with them because human experience is all nonrelativistic, having to do with motion which is slow compared to the speed of light. Moreover, according to the theory of relativity, at the speed of light, particles have energy and momentum and angular momentum (spin) without mass.

As has been emphasized before, the speed of light has nothing special to do with light. It is really the natural speed limit of the universe and is achieved by *any* massless particle, in particular by the photon. It just happens to be called the speed of light because the photons of light* are the only massless particles whose speed has been accurately clocked.

In addition to their common speed, the massless particles have in common their stability. The law of energy conservation imposes the "downhill" rule for spontaneous decay: The masses of the product particles must be less than the mass of the parent. If the parent has no mass, there are obviously no possible lighter products, so that its decay is forbidden by energy conservation. The stability of the massless particles can be deduced from quite a different argument, having to do again with the peculiarities of high-speed travel. Relativity predicts that the scale of time—the actual rhythm of nature, so to speak—is slowed down for particles moving at high speed. At the end of Chapter Three, the influence of this time dilation on the lifetime of pions was discussed. Fast pions live longer than slow pions, and the more closely they approach to the speed of light, the longer their characteristic life span becomes. If they could be made to move precisely at the speed of light, they would live forever. The massless particles, which do move at the speed of light, are truly ageless. For them time has come to a standstill. Even if their decay violated no conservation law, they would still live forever, for to them forever is no time at all. The photon, in perfect harmony with the universe, never gets any older. One might say that it is traveling with time.

Stability does not mean that a particle cannot be caused to disappear. An electron is stable, which means that, left to itself, it will

---

* By "light" is meant any electromagnetic radiation (radar, for example) not merely what the human eye can see. The speed of light is very accurately known. It is 2.99793×10^{10} cm/sec.

never spontaneously vanish. But if it meets a positron, both it and the positron will vanish in a puff of photons. The photon and neutrinos likewise would live forever in empty space, but in interaction with matter they may disappear. The photon does so very easily, the neutrinos only rarely.

In spite of their distinctiveness, the massless particles definitely belong to the family of particles and resemble the massive particles in more ways than they differ. All of the particles have certain non-common-sense peculiarities; the massless particles merely have these in greatest measure. The electron, for example, can never be brought precisely to rest, for this would imply, according to the uncertainty principle, an infinite uncertainty in its position. The photon is worse; it can not be slowed down at all. The electron can be localized approximately in a small region, but because of its wave nature, can never be precisely located at a point. The photon can not even be approximately localized. But photons and neutrinos, like all other particles, can be created and annihilated, have wavelike properties, carry energy, momentum, and angular momentum, and are governed by laws of probability.

One necessary condition for masslessness seems to be the absence of charge. Every charged particle has mass, although not every neutral particle is massless. There does exist some theoretical understanding—rather technical in nature—of the reasons why photons and neutrinos are massless, but why the other particles have the masses they do have, and why there is not a larger family of massless particles, remains a mystery.

The Photon

Interest in the nature of light must go back to prehistory. It is undoubtedly as old as any problem in science, and probably one of the most rewarding scientific problems ever tackled. Interwoven with the whole history of modern physics, from the 17th century to the present, is the study of light, which has been closely tied to the development of the theories of electromagnetism, relativity, and quantum mechanics, as well as to the practical science of optics, to numerous discoveries in mathematics and, in the modern period, to such things as radar and infrared photography. From Ole Römer's measurement of the speed of light by observations of the times of appearance of the moons of Jupiter (1675) to a recent precision measurement of the internal magnetism of the muon (1961), the history of the study of light has closely paralleled the over-all history of physics, whose frontier has moved in those 300 years from the solar system to the elementary particles. (What magnetism has to do with light will be indicated below.) The fascinating history has not yet ended, for in spite of the remarkable amount we know about light, there remain a few puzzles which we recognize (plus, undoubtedly, puzzles not yet suspected).

The fact that light moves at a definite, albeit enormous, speed, and not infinitely rapidly, has been known since Römer's measurement and many successive measurements have determined this speed with great precision. By 1700 several important facts about light were known. White light was known to consist of a mixture of colors. Light was known to be deflected upon passing from one medium to another, the amount of deflection depending on the color. The speed of light in empty space was known to be the same for all colors (otherwise a moon of Jupiter would appear one color upon first appearance from behind Jupiter, later other colors, or white). Light was known to travel in straight lines in a uniform medium. It was known to carry energy. And a peculiar phenomenon called double refraction was known: upon entering some crystals, light undergoes not one deflection but two at once, splitting into two separate beams.

In spite of this knowledge and a good deal more accumulated during the eighteenth century, the nature of light remained a mystery for another hundred years. The fundamental question to be decided was: Does light consist of particles or is it a wave phenomenon? When the wave theory triumphed early in the nineteenth century, the defeated adherents of the particle theory could scarcely have imagined that after another hundred years light would turn out to consist of particles after all, leading to the modern resolution of the argument: Light is *both* wave and particle.

Given the facts that light travels at a fixed speed in straight lines through empty space carrying energy from one place to another, a quite natural first guess is that light must consist of a stream of particles. This is the view commonly believed to have been championed by Newton, although, in fact, Newton recognized that the evidence was inadequate to decide one way or the other about the nature of light. The particle interpretation merely seemed to him to be the simplest consistent with the known facts. The bending of light as it enters a different substance can be explained if it is assumed that the light particles speed up in denser matter. Double refraction was unexplained, but the alternate wave theory did not seem to explain it either. There were, however, a few problems with the particle idea. Since no one had thought of the possibility of massless particles, it seemed surprising that an object giving off light apparently lost no weight, and an object absorbing light gained no weight. The invariable speed of light was also not easily explained with particles. One might suppose that the particles of different colors of light should travel at different speeds, or that a more intense source of light should give off faster particles of light.

The wave theory accounted nicely for these two difficulties. A wave can transmit energy without conducting mass from one place to another, and it is a common feature of waves to have a fixed speed, independent of their strength and of their wavelength. The speed of sound, for example, does not depend on the intensity or the pitch. The bending of waves by refraction is also easy to understand, but it requires that the wave move more slowly in the denser medium, rather than more quickly. (In the mid-nineteenth century, experiment decided in favor of the slowing down and lent further support to the wave idea, which was rather firmly established by then.)

The difficulty with the wave idea seemed to be that it required an all-pervasive substance filling space that could transmit the light vibrations. The ether invented for this purpose had to be indeed a very ethereal substance, for, unlike water and air, it had to be totally transparent and frictionless, offering no impediment to the passage of material objects through it. (Otherwise, the earth would be slowed down and spiral into the sun.) In spite of these unlikely properties, the ether was acceptable to most scientists. It already seemed to be necessary to explain how gravitational and electric forces could act through empty space. The idea of action at a distance with no transmitting agent seemed more repugnant to most men than did the idea of a mysterious ether.

Quite independent of arguments and speculation about the ether, a series of experiments in the first two decades of the nineteenth century so strongly supported the wave idea that there could no longer be any doubt that light was a wave motion. It is true that the diehard exponents of the light particles offered some tortured and implausible explanations of these phenomena, but the same phenomena were so simply and beautifully explained with the light waves that there could be little doubt that the wave nature of light offered the "right" explanation. It is important to note at this point that these experiments, which led to the triumph of the wave theory, are as valid today as they were 150 years ago. In spite of our deeper knowledge which leads us now to say that light does, after all, consist of particles—photons—the old experiments cannot be rejected. They may be repeated today with the same results and with the same interpretation in terms of waves. We must accept the new evidence that light is particlelike, but we must retain the old evidence that light is wavelike. Fortunately, the theory of quantum mechanics has come along to explain how light can be both and how all particles can be both.

The conclusive evidence for the wave nature of light came through the phenomena of diffraction and interference (defined and discussed in Chapter Three). A wave passing an obstacle does not leave a precise sharp shadow, but is deflected a little into the dark region, giving the shadow a slightly fuzzy edge. This is *diffraction*. Two waves arriving at the same point may strengthen each other if they are crest to crest and trough to trough, or they may cancel each other out if the crest of one coincides with the trough of the other. This is *interference*. A little thought will show that each of these phenomena would be rather difficult to explain in terms of light particles. The wave theory, of course, did more than give a qualitative explanation of the existence of these phenomena. It provided a quantitative theory of diffraction and interference which accorded perfectly with the experimental facts. The exact way in which the light intensity varies smoothly through the region of the fuzzy shadow edge, for example, is predicted, as is the pattern of interference resulting from two sources of light (see Figure 3.4).

The same phenomena which proved the existence of light waves provided a tool for measuring wavelength and it was soon learned that different colors are distinguished by different wavelengths. Visible light spans about one octave* of wavelength, from short-wave violet, 3.5×10^{-5} cm, to long-wave red, 7×10^{-5} cm. Although

---

* An octave represents a factor-of-two change in wavelength or frequency. Middle C, for example, is 256 cycles per second (c.p.s.), the C one octave higher is 512 c.p.s., and the next C (high C) is 1,024 c.p.s.

small, these wavelengths are still several thousand times larger than the size of an atom, which is about 10^{-8} cm.

Besides wavelength, a wave can be characterized by its frequency, that is, its number of vibrations per second. Light waves vibrate extremely rapidly, more than 10^{14} cycles per second. The highest pitched sound audible to the human ear is about 10^4 cycles per second. Radio waves vibrate at about 10^6 (one million) cycles per second in the ordinary band on up to near 10^9 (one billion) cycles per second in what is called the UHF (ultra high frequency) band. The vibrations of light are about one million times more rapid than the UHF vibrations, and the wavelength, correspondingly, a million times shorter. Frequency and wavelength are related by a very simple formula:

$$\lambda f = v,$$

where λ is the wavelength (for example, in centimeters), f is the frequency (for example, in vibrations per second), and v is the speed of the wave (for example, in centimeters per second). The formula can be used for any wave at all. Thus, for the standard musical A, f equals 440 cycles per second. The speed of sound in air is 3×10^4 cm/sec, so the wavelength in air of the tone A is its speed v divided by its frequency f, which turns out to be about 68 cm. We could use the same formula, for example, to calculate the frequency of green light whose wavelength is 5×10^{-5} cm. Its speed of 3×10^{10} cm/sec divided by this wavelength gives its frequency of 6×10^{14} vibrations per second.

The next great advance in the understanding of light came just about 100 years ago, around 1860, mainly from the work of the British mathematical physicist, James Maxwell. This advance came not directly from the study of light, but circuitously from the study of electricity and magnetism. The intimate connection between electricity and magnetism had been fully appreciated for only a few decades, and Maxwell sought to synthesize what was known of electricity and magnetism into a few simple equations that might serve as the basis of the theory of the combined science of electromagnetism. In what was one of the most stunning scientific achievements of the nineteenth century (or of any period), Maxwell succeeded in discovering a simple set of equations that not only accounted for every known electrical and magnetic phenomenon, but (as an unexpected bonus) also accounted for light. Maxwell discovered that his equations predicted that combined electric and magnetic disturbances (fields) should be capable of propagating as waves through empty space.

An interesting aspect of electricity is how differently it behaves when in motion than when at rest. Consider, for example, a laboratory containing a number of electrically charged objects and a number of magnets, all at different points and all at rest. The electrified objects exert forces on each other and the magnets exert forces on each other, but there is no interaction at all between the electricity and the magnetism. This is attributed to the existence of two distinct "fields," or disturbances in space, the electric field and the magnetic field. The observations with stationary charges and magnets are successfully interpreted by postulating that a charge at rest creates only an electric field and reacts only to an electric field. Correspondingly, a magnet at rest creates only a magnetic field and reacts only to a magnetic field. Like the intersecting beams of two searchlights, the two stationary fields coexist in space without mutual interaction. However, when motion of charges or magnets is involved, the situation changes drastically. A moving charge influences a magnet and a moving magnet influences a charge. Either a charge or a magnet, when in motion, generates both an electric field and a magnetic field. These coupled fields are called electromagnetic fields. In the period 1800–1840 the links between electricity and magnetism arising from motion had been discovered and explored, and it was these (along with older static laws) which Maxwell's equations elegantly summarized, making it clear that electricity and magnetism were merely two aspects of the same thing.

Maxwell's bonus had to do with the electromagnetic link induced by motion, or change. His equations predicted that, under certain conditions, electromagnetic fields should be able to travel through space. Whether originally produced by moving charges or magnets, once produced, they should propagate independently as electromagnetic waves. These propagating-wave solutions to Maxwell's equations occurred only when the electric and magnetic fields were present with equal intensity and both were constantly oscillating, or vibrating. Under these circumstances, the electromagnetic wave should proceed through space at a speed which Maxwell calculated solely from the known laws of electricity and magnetism.

The predicted speed was 3×10^{10} cm/sec, exactly (within experimental error) the known speed of light. It was but a short step for Maxwell then to suggest that light was nothing more than an electromagnetic wave.

The successful prediction of the speed of light would have been almost enough to make this suggestion at once acceptable, but its correctness was confirmed in several other ways. There were already some hints of a connection between electricity and light, and there was a strong hint that matter, which radiates light, had an electrical basis; that is, that there is charge within every atom. Maxwell's theory also predicted that light was a transverse vibration, not a longitudinal vibration. A water wave is a simple example of a transverse vibration. The motion of the *water* is up and down, transverse to the motion of the *wave*, which is horizontal. A swimmer is lifted up and down as a wave passes by. But sound waves or shock waves which pass through a medium rather than over its surface are longitudinal—the material vibrates in the direction in which the wave is proceeding. A man struck by a shock wave from an explosion is first pushed away from the explosion, then sucked back toward it; thus he is caused to vibrate along the direction of the wave motion. Early adherents of the wave theory of light quite naturally thought of light passing through the ether as analogous to sound passing through the air, vibrating longitudinally. But several effects, including double refraction, had shown that light must be a transverse wave. Maxwell's theory indeed required that the electric and magnetic fields in the light wave should be vibrating transverse to the direction of motion (and to each other). For a wave traveling north, the electric field might be vibrating up and down and the magnetic field vibrating east and west. Or the wave could be a mixture of many different directions of vibration, but all perpendicular to the direction of motion. When the latter type of wave enters a crystal, it is not surprising if it gets split into two beams. The speed within the crystal could (and sometimes does) depend upon the direction of vibration of the electric field, so that part of the beam is refracted through one angle, part through another angle. Why there cannot be more than two beams is a technical point we will not endeavor to explain. For a longitudinal wave there is only one possible direction for the vibration; hence there is no basis for explaining double refraction.

Considering the equation $\lambda f = c$ (c is the usual symbol for the constant speed of light), Maxwell observed that there should be a vast electromagnetic spectrum extending from arbitrarily small wavelengths (and correspondingly high frequencies) to arbitrarily large wavelengths (and low frequencies). Of this infinite range, the single octave of visible light was an insignificant sliver. Knowing of the theoretical existence of this unlimited spectrum and producing electromagnetic radiation in practice, however, were two different things. The production of electromagnetic radiation requires the vibration of charge, but slow vibration, such as shaking a charged object back and forth by hand, is very ineffective. Atoms, fortunately, co-operate in causing charge to vibrate rapidly, for the electrons within atoms are in a constant state of oscillatory motion with frequencies of 10^{14} cycles per second and more. They can be caused to emit light readily. As we now know, nuclei emit still higher-frequency electromagnetic radiation, known as gamma rays, because the charged protons within nuclei vibrate at still greater frequencies, about 10^{20} times per second.

High-frequency oscillation of charge was difficult to produce in Maxwell's time, and it was not until the 1880's that David Hughes in England and Heinrich Hertz in Germany succeeded in generating electromagnetic radiation "artificially," that is, with man-made vibration of charge rather than with the natural atomic vibrations. Hughes and Hertz used the vibration of charge in a spark, whose frequency is "only" one million to one hundred million vibrations per second (10^6 to 10^8). In so doing they verified details of Maxwell's predictions of the properties of electromagnetic radiation and so indirectly lent further support to the electromagnetic-wave interpretation of light.

By the end of the nineteenth century the combined theory of electricity, magnetism, radio waves, and light seemed to be in beautiful and finished form. Physicists had come to accept the ether and its ability to vibrate transversely while eluding all direct observation as a necessary fact of life, and the wave nature of light and other forms of radiation was established beyond doubt. Yet a few surprises were left. Within the first few years of this century, the photon made its appearance and the ether was discarded.

The vanishing of the ether, made necessary by the theory of relativity, brought about a revolutionary change in man's view of empty space. Although it occurred at about the same time, the change was not directly connected with the discovery of the photon, and we shall postpone further discussion of the ether to Chapter Seven.

The photon was "discovered" by two theoretical physicists—Max Planck in Germany in 1899 and Albert Einstein in Switzerland in 1905. That is, each suggested that if light came in discrete bundles of energy rather than in continuous waves, certain puzzling experiments could be explained. Although Planck's discovery came first, it is considerably more difficult to understand than Einstein's. It is concerned with the way in which energy is distributed inside a closed box within which electromagnetic waves are bouncing back and forth. The waves themselves carry energy that is continuously being exchanged with the energy of atoms in the walls, and the problem Planck set out to solve was how to explain the way in which all the available energy was distributed—some of it in the walls, some of it in the radiation, and that in the radiation divided among waves of different frequencies. This is a complex system of many atoms and many wavelengths. Planck found that he could explain how the available energy was shared among the various parts of this system only if he postulated that the part of the energy carried by the waves was carried in bundles of a certain definite size, given by the formula:

$$E = hf,$$

where E is the energy in one bundle of radiation—or one photon, as we would say now—and f is the frequency of the radiation. The constant h in this formula is a constant of proportionality, providing a hitherto unsuspected link—between the frequency of a light wave and the smallest bundle of energy which can be carried by that light wave. This quantum constant, which we have already encountered in discussing spin, is called Planck's constant in honor of its discoverer.

There are two points worth noticing about this formula. One is the proportionality of energy to frequency. The photon of a high-frequency nuclear gamma ray carries much more energy than the photon of a low-frequency radio wave, in fact about 10^{14} times more. A single gamma ray has so much energy that it is very easily detected by itself. A single photon leaving the antenna of a radio broadcasting station has so little energy that it is undetectable. Only the combined effect of a vast army of radio photons can be detected, and when many photons act in consort, their individual-particle aspect is overwhelmed by the over-all wave aspect. The radio engineer never has to be concerned with individual photons and can think always in terms of waves. The nuclear physicist, on the other hand, thinks of gamma rays primarily as particles, and is less concerned with their wave aspect.

The second point is the significance of the size of Planck's constant h. If h were much smaller, the amount of energy in one photon would be smaller and the quantum aspect, or particle aspect, of light would be less noticeable. If we imagined h disappearing altogether, becoming zero, then there would be no photons and light would be purely waves again. On the other hand, if h were much larger, the quantum aspect of light would be more noticeable. Single photons would carry so much energy that they might be separately observed as flashes of light by the eye of man. (This is pure fiction, for if h really *were* larger, atoms would be larger, and man would be larger too. This discussion is only for the purpose of clarifying the meaning of h, whose size, of course, can not be manipulated.) What Planck's constant does is to determine the scale of the quantum world. We live in a classical world, because the energies of our everyday experience—the energy of raising a hand, the energy of reading a page—are very large compared to the energy of a single photon of light.

Einstein saw the need of the photon to account for a different and very much simpler phenomenon than the one considered by Planck. Planck considered a system composed of a vast number of atoms and of photons; Einstein considered an experiment involving the elementary event of the absorption of a single photon. His paper in 1905 on the photoelectric effect led again to Planck's equation $E = hf$ and made the photon seem an inescapable necessity.

A few years earlier, it had been noticed that when ultraviolet light (invisible light with frequency somewhat greater, and wavelength somewhat smaller, than those of the violet end of the visible spectrum) shone upon the surface of some metals, electrons were emitted from the surface. This phenomenon, christened the photoelectric effect, could be understood qualitatively in terms of Maxwell's wave theory of light, but that theory failed entirely to account for the quantitative details of the process. According to the wave theory, the electromagnetic radiation striking the surface set electrons near the surface into motion, and some of these were caused to move so rapidly that they could escape and fly off from the surface.

The wave theory had two main predictions to make, and both were in disagreement with the facts. First, more intense radiation should have pushed harder on the electrons, and caused them to fly off with more energy. Instead, the energy of the departing electrons did not vary as the light was made more intense. The only change was that a larger number of electrons escaped. Second, according to the wave idea, the electron energy should not depend particularly upon the frequency of the light, as long as sufficient light intensity shone on the surface. In fact, higher-frequency radiation caused the electrons to fly off more energetically, even if the intensity was lowered. Below some particular frequency, no electrons at all escaped. Ordinary visible light (of lower frequency than ultraviolet) was incapable of ejecting any electrons, however intensely it shone on the surface.

Einstein noticed that the photon theory of light could explain the observed facts of the photoelectric effect very simply and elegantly. According to the wave idea, an electron gradually absorbed energy from the wave, and could absorb any amount, large or small. Suppose instead, said Einstein, that energy can be absorbed from the incoming light only in bundles of a certain definite size. An electron either absorbs exactly one whole photon, or it absorbs none. Increasing the intensity of the light increases the number of photons, but does not change the energy of each one. The higher intensity results in more electrons absorbing photons, but does not increase the amount of energy absorbed by any one. If the energy of each photon follows Planck's equation,

$$E = hf,$$

then the energy absorbed by a given electron depends on the frequency of the impinging light but not on its intensity. The chance that one electron absorbs more than one photon is negligible, because the number of photons is much lower than the number of electrons. It is as if the outfield of a baseball park were filled up with a few thousand outfielders (electrons), and a few dozen balls (photons) were batted to them. Most of the fielders would catch no balls. A few would catch one. The chance that any one fielder would catch more than one ball would be very small indeed. To make the analogy a bit closer to the actual photoelectric effect, we should say that as soon as a fielder catches a ball he feels so good (gains enough energy) that he runs to the fence and leaps out of the field. He would have very little chance of intercepting a second ball on the way out. The enthusiasm with which he departs would, therefore, be determined by the energy of the single ball caught. If the number of balls batted (intensity of the light) were increased, the number of fielders leaving the field would increase, but the energy with which each leaped out would be the same. If, on the other hand, each ball were batted out more forcefully (higher-energy photons), the successful catcher would be more jubilant and would bound out with more energy. If the balls were batted out with very little energy (low-frequency photons), no fielder would quite have the energy to leap the fence after catching one. In spite of a heavy bombardment, no fielders would be seen emerging from the ball park.

The two basic facts about the photoelectric effect—that the number of electrons depends on the intensity of the light, and that the energy of each electron depends on the frequency of the light—were simply explained by the photon hypothesis, while being entirely unexplainable by the wave theory. In the photoelectric effect, one was witnessing the single events of photon absorption by electrons, much simpler than the complex system considered by Planck, and there was no recourse but to accept the photon as part of reality, in spite of all of the accumulated evidence for the wave nature of light. From measurements of the frequency of the light and the energy of the electrons, it was possible to determine the value of Planck's constant h, and to verify the correctness of the photon equation, $E = hf$. The photon had arrived to join the electron as one of nature's elementary particles, and had brought with it a new fundamental quantum constant of nature, h, which was to make its way into the fully developed quantum theory twenty years later. In the hands of Planck and Einstein, the fact that the photon energy was proportional to the frequency of the light was arbitrarily introduced in order to account for experimental facts. The equation $E = hf$ was in 1905 a *law* of nature, but did not rest on any underlying general theory until 1925, when the quantum theory, which accounts for the behavior of all of the elementary particles, including the photon, was discovered.

Now that the photon has been "demoted" so that it is just one among many particles, what is of special interest about it to the physicist, and what is its special role in the life of man? Let us consider the second question first. This is easy, for the life of man is unthinkable without the photon. Without photons, we would not see, and we would also not be, for the ultimate source of almost all of the energy on the earth is the supply of photons arriving from the sun. Electrical engineers speak of power engineering and communication engineering. In the cosmos, photons are the principal instrument of both. Most of the energy and most of the information carried from one part of the universe to another is carried by photons. The earth is bathed continually in photons. Those from the sun bring energy, those from other stars and other galaxies bring us information about the rest of the universe as well as energy. The unique aspect of the photon is that it is very readily created and very readily absorbed in the presence of matter, but in empty space can travel on forever. The earth is also bathed in neutrinos, but these have been inconsequential, because it is very difficult to absorb them and they generally pass through the earth and its residents as if nothing were there. Compare this with an easily stopped photon. If you look at your own hand in sunlight you see only its outer surface. Photons that have traveled one hundred million miles through empty space are stopped dead in less than one millionth of a centimeter when they penetrate solid matter. (The phenomenon of reflection of sunlight—for example, from the skin—actually involves the absorption and re-emission of photons.)

On the earth itself, photons play a less important role in the transmission of power, but dominate the scene in the transmission of information. Radio, television, radar, light signals, infrared photography, and x ray pictures all represent examples of the transmission of information by photons. In the United States, the Federal Communications Commission exists to regulate the demand for photons. Photons also provide a principle source of information about atoms (which emit light and x rays) and about nuclei (which emit still higher-frequency gamma rays). Every kind of atom and every kind of nucleus is capable of emitting photons of only certain characteristic frequencies (or energies), so that the pattern of photons emitted provides a unique identifying "signature" for the atom or nucleus. Aside from its usefulness in research, this phenomenon provides an easy way to determine the components of an unknown substance, or to detect impurities in nearly pure substances.

The comings and goings of photons are dictated by the motion of charged particles. Any particle with charge can emit or absorb a photon, but electrons, being the lightest, most easily moved charged particles, are responsible for most of the emission and absorption of photons both in the atomic world and in the macroscopic world. Within an atom, an electron may jump to a low-energy state of motion and emit a photon, or it may absorb a photon and jump to a higher-energy state of motion. In the antenna of a radio broadcasting station the oscillatory motion of electrons back and forth results in the emission of photons. Some of these photons striking the antenna of a home radio receiver are absorbed by electrons, whose resulting motion is communicated by electrical signals to the interior of the radio set. No matter which photon process is being considered, the chain of events is always the same. Somewhere, a charged particle in motion emits a photon. That photon may travel a tiny fraction of a centimeter or it may travel billions of miles, but eventually the photon encounters another charged particle which can absorb it with a consequent change in the particle's motion. Usually, the kind of motion that created the photon is the kind of motion that results from its absorption. The light from an atomic vibration is absorbed by an atom. The radio photons created in the antenna wire set electrons in another antenna wire into vibration.

There is one more story to tell about photons. This is the role in nature of a shadowy kind of photon called a virtual photon, a photon that is emitted and again absorbed by the same charged particle without ever quite being released and sent on its way. This almost-but-not-quite photon has played an important role in the very recent history of science; it will be discussed in Chapter Seven.

The Neutrinos

The electron's neutrino was "invented" in 1930 by Wolfgang Pauli to save nature's conservation laws. This unobtrusive little particle with no mass and no charge salvaged three of the absolute conservation laws from wreckage, a task so heroic that its existence came to be an article of faith among physicists, even though it escaped direct observation until 1956. Like the antiproton and antineutron (which were observed in 1955 and 1956), the neutrino was long a ghostly member of the elementary-particle zoo, necessary to the structure of modern physics, but itself not directly observed.

After the discovery of the muon, the duties placed upon the shoulders of the neutrino increased, for the muon, as well as the electron, required a neutrino partner. Now we know that there are two distinct neutrinos (at least), one for the electron and one for the muon. But since these two particles are so nearly identical, we shall in this section usually refer simply to "the neutrino." How did it come about that this particle which no one had ever observed could establish itself as an essential part of the submicroscopic world?

Historically, the neutrino was postulated to save the law of energy conservation. It very soon became also the savior of the laws of momentum conservation and angular-momentum conservation; eventually it contributed to the laws of electron-family and muon-family conservation.

When a typical heavy radioactive nucleus emits an alpha particle, the alpha particle shoots out with a well-defined energy, always the same for a particular type of nucleus. The daughter nucleus left behind is lighter than the radioactive parent nucleus, and the difference in mass multiplied by the square of the speed of light is an energy which is exactly equal to the energy taken away by the alpha particle—its energy of being (mass) plus its energy of motion (kinetic energy). In short, the books are balanced; the energy is conserved. The energy of the parent nucleus is equal to the energy of the daugther nucleus plus the energy of the alpha particle (remembering always that mass must be included in the energy balance). Similarly, in the phenomenon of gamma decay, a particular nucleus emits a characteristic-energy photon which carries away exactly the energy lost by the nucleus.* In the third kind of natural radioactivity, beta decay, the books appeared not

---

* In fact, a particular kind of nucleus may emit gamma rays or alpha particles of several different energies because the daughter nucleus may be left behind in several different energy states. If a lower-energy photon or alpha particle is ejected, the daughter is left with more than its normal energy and exists in what is called an excited state. The conservation of energy has been verified separately for each energy of photon or alpha particle.

to be balanced. A collection of identical beta-active nuclei did not all emit beta particles (electrons) of the same energy, or even of a fixed set of energies; instead, the electrons came out in a "continuous spectrum" with all possible energies from zero up to some maximum value. When an electron of the maximum energy was ejected, it was just sufficient to account for the energy difference between parent and daughter nucleus. When a lower-energy electron was ejected, the energy books were out of balance and some energy remained unaccounted for.

Some physicists were willing to abandon the law of energy conservation. It is, after all, a law founded on experiment, they argued, and if experiment fails to confirm it, it must be abandoned. Energy was known to be conserved in the macroscopic world and in the atomic world, but perhaps it failed in the nuclear and subnuclear domains, just as the laws of classical mechanics had failed in the atomic domain. If this were true, the phenomenon of beta decay would be a vital key to understanding deeper layers of nature.

Pauli suggested instead that a neutral particle, which escaped detection, might be emitted from the nucleus along with the electron, with the available energy shared between this new particle (the neutrino) and the electron. This proposal could at once explain why the electrons observed in beta decay could fly off with any energy up to some maximum, for they could carry away any fraction of the total available energy, the neutrino taking the rest. The neutrino had to be assumed to be neutral for, if charged, its electric interaction would have caused it to be readily observable. Moreover, that would have led to nonconservation of charge, a high price to pay for preserving the conservation of energy. In addition, the neutrino had to be assumed to have a very small mass. When the electron departed with its maximum energy, little or no energy would be left over for the neutrino. But if the neutrino had a mass, it could never have less energy than its own mass energy. Only experimental inaccuracy prevented deciding exactly how small the neutrino mass must be. Now it is known to be less than one thousandth of the electron mass, and is believed almost certainly to be exactly zero. The neutrino, christened in Italian by Enrico Fermi, is the "little neutral one."

Which was the more radical proposal: the nonconservation of energy, or the introduction of a new particle? Now we should have no hesitation in deciding, for the list of particles has grown so large that merely adding one more would not be very radical. But, in 1930, Pauli's suggestion appeared much more daring than it might today. Then, only the proton, electron, and photon were known. Nevertheless, the abandonment of energy conservation would, even then, have been more revolutionary. On the experimental side, energy conservation was already verified in the nuclear processes of gamma decay and alpha decay. Even more important, energy conservation was founded upon a deep and simple symmetry of nature, the uniformity of time—the principle that all physical experiments should yield the same results at one time as at another. Giving up energy conservation would have been much more disruptive of fundamental ideas in science than was the introduction of a new particle.

Yet regardless of convictions based upon the beauty and simplicity of natural law, this question, like every other in science, had to be decided eventually by experiment. The neutrino hypothesis came to be accepted because it made possible a simple and successful theory of the phenomenon of beta decay, and because it led to the saving of several more conservation laws besides energy conservation. Finally, in 1956, the electron's neutrino was directly observed; in 1962 the muon's neutrino was observed and discovered to be a different particle.

According to Pauli's original suggestion, the neutrino existed within the nucleus and was emitted during the process of beta decay,* along with an electron which had also been present. Several years later (1934), in constructing a mathematical theory of beta decay, Fermi took advantage of part of Pauli's suggestion but introduced a very radical and significant innovation of his own. The discovery of the neutron in the meantime (1932) had made it clear that electrons did not exist within the nucleus, and there was no reason to think that neutrinos did either. "Suppose," reasoned Fermi, "that the electron and antineutrino are only created at the moment of their emission, and that, simultaneously, a neutron within the nucleus is transformed into a proton." In symbols,

$$n \rightarrow p + e^- + \bar{\nu}_e.$$

---

* Pauli at first wanted the neutrino within the nucleus to account for some unexplained facts about nuclear spin as well. This job later fell on the neutron.

Fermi's theory, aside from strongly bolstering Pauli's proposal of the neutrino, had a special significance in the history of modern physics. It was the first successful theory of the creation and annihilation of material particles. Previously, only photons had been known to be created and destroyed. Developments since Fermi advanced his theory have shown that processes of annihilation and creation probably govern *all* of the fundamental interactions in nature.

Figure 4.7 (page 101) illustrates the beta decay of a single free neutron, showing the paths and directions of spin of the particles.

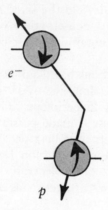

Figure 5.1. What can be measured in beta decay. If there were no neutrino, this, instead of Figure 4.7, would picture the result of the decay of a neutron.

Although the antineutrino is pictured, it is in fact unseen. Only the tracks of the electron and proton can actually be observed (for example, in a cloud chamber). With greater difficulty, the spins of electron and proton may also be observed.

Now we can see how, without the neutrino, four fundamental conservation laws would be violated. First, the energies do not balance. Electron energy plus proton energy add up to less than the initial neutron energy (its rest mass). The neutrino was invented to fill this gap. Second, as Figure 5.1 shows, momentum appears not to be conserved. Since the neutron is intitially at rest, it has no momentum. To preserve zero momentum, the electron and proton would have to fly off back to back, with equal and opposite momenta cancelling to zero. In fact, they do not. But the neutrino, which has the right energy to save the conservation of energy, also has some momentum, and this turns out to be exactly the momentum needed to combine with the momenta of electron and proton to make all three together add up to zero. At no extra charge (with no additional assumptions) the neutrino has saved a second and equally fundamental conservation law. The existence of this particle begins to seem quite believable.

Without the neutrino, angular momentum would not be conserved. In Figure 5.1, for example, electron and proton spins are cancelling, but the initial neutron had a nonzero spin. If the neutrino is supposed to have one-half unit of spin itself, then it can add to its chores the saving of angular-momentum conservation. The neutrino spin has never been measured directly, but there is ample indirect evidence, for example, from successful predictions of beta-decay phenomena from Fermi's theory, that it does indeed have one-half unit of spin.

Finally, the electron's neutrino saves the law of electron-family conservation, for the antineutrino accompanying the electron gives a total electron-family number of zero, the same after the decay as before. Actually, the law of electron-family conservation was only suggested *after* the neutrino had come to be accepted. Since the underlying symmetry principle upon which this law is based is unknown, we could not claim at the present stage of history to be upset if the law were violated. Nevertheless, the empirical evidence supports this conservation law, and it is a good guess that there exists an undiscovered symmetry principle upon which it is founded. If this is so, then we should be as disturbed *ex post facto* by a breakdown of the law of electron-family conservation as we now would be by any violation of the laws of energy, momentum, and angular momentum conservation, which are based upon the uniformity of space and time.

Details of the Fermi theory of beta decay are out of place here, but it is important to be aware that the neutrino in this theory did much more than preserve four conservation laws. It made possible specific predictions about the fraction of electrons that come out in each direction and with each energy, and predictions about the relative rates of beta decay of different radioactive nuclei, all of which have been verified by experiment. (Actually there were some ambiguities in the Fermi theory which were resolved only in

1957.) In addition, the Fermi theory has been extended with perfect success from the decay of the neutron to the decay of the muon, given by

$$\mu^- \rightarrow \nu_\mu + e^- + \overline{\nu}_e.$$

This is also a beta-decay process, for in it an electron is created along with its antineutrino.

The process in nature whereby a stable particle comes into existence is usually quite similar to the process whereby it is absorbed, or annihilated. Thus, a photon is born by the oscillation of electric charge and, upon absorption, sets charge into motion. An electron may be born simultaneously with its antiparticle, the positron; it can die if it meets a positron with which to annihilate. The neutrino comes into existence in processes of beta decay or other decay processes which collectively are classified as the weak interactions. It can therefore be absorbed and observed only via further weak interactions. In this lies the key to understanding the difficulty of observing the neutrino. It is observable only when it interacts in some way with matter, but the chance that it interacts—and such interaction always involves its annihilation—is very small indeed.

It will be sufficient here to consider the particular process that was first used to catch the elusive neutrino (actually the antineutrino). An antineutrino may be born in the beta decay process,

$$n \rightarrow p + e^- + \overline{\nu}_e.$$

If this antineutrino later encounters another proton, it may, with a certain very small probability, be annihilated in what is known as the inverse beta-decay process

$$\overline{\nu}_e + p \rightarrow n + e^+.$$

Proton and antineutrino disappear, and a neutron and positron are created. The capture process involves the same particles as the creation process—except that the laws of charge conservation and electron-family conservation require the *antielectron*, or positron, to appear in the capture process, whereas the electron appeared in the creation process.

Can we estimate the chance of capturing an antineutrino in this way? It is easy to do and the result is rather startling, providing a clear demonstration that a few minutes is a very long time in the elementary-particle world. We start with the fact that a free neutron, on the average, lives about 17 minutes, or 1000 seconds, before it spontaneously undergoes beta decay, turning into a proton plus electron and antineutrino. This means that if another antineutrino of comparable energy is in contact with a proton for about 17 minutes, it will be captured and stimulate the process of inverse beta decay. Since an antineutrino travels always at the speed of light, it will not stick close to any proton for seventeen minutes, not even for a small fraction of a second; but as it travels through matter, it will be exposed to many protons, one after the other, each for an instant, and the inverse beta decay will occur on the average after a total exposure of about 17 minutes. (The precise time depends on the antineutrino energy, and on exactly what nuclei the antineutrino is brushing by on its flight through matter, but the figure 17 minutes will do for our rough estimate.)

In 17 minutes an antineutrino moves 5×10^{11} cm, about twice the distance from earth to sun, which is an eight-minute trip. Now imagine a solid wall 5×10^{11} cm thick. Picture the antineutrino as it flies through this wall, a tiny fuzzy ball whose size is about equal to its own wavelength, say 4×10^{-11} cm, about one five-hundredth the diameter of an atom. The wave nature of the antineutrino is all-important. If it were truly a point particle, it would have practically no chance at all of striking the nucleus as it passed through an atom. But the wave nature of particles enables the antineutrino to reach out, to make its presence felt out to a distance of its wavelength. This wavelength, however, is short, and the effective size of the antineutrino is still tiny compared with the size of an atom. If we could take a series of snapshots of our fuzzy, extended antineutrino as it passed through matter, we should almost always see it occupying a space between nuclei, not actually touching a nucleus. Only one in many snapshots would show it in contact with a nucleus. So, after spending 17 minutes traveling through the 200-million-mile solid wall, the antineutrino has been exposed to protons within nuclei a great deal less than 17 minutes, for most of the time it was not touching a nucleus at all. In fact it spent only about one hundred-millionth of that time in contact with nuclei, so that the thickness of the wall must be extended one hundred million times before the required 17-minute total contact between antineutrinos and protons is achieved. The antineutrino would have to penetrate into a solid wall an average distance of 2×10^{16}

miles, or 3500 light-years, before it would be absorbed and induce the inverse beta decay reaction! This distance, two hundred million times greater than the earth-sun separation, is about a tenth the size of our galaxy.

It is instructive to carry out a similar calculation for a photon of visible light. To begin with, an atom requires only about 10^{-8} sec (one one-hundred-millionth of a second) to emit such a photon. This photon needs to spend only about 10^{-8} sec in contact with an atom in order to be absorbed. In 10^{-8} sec, a photon proceeds about 300 cm (10 feet). However, our photon is so large that, at any given instant, it encompasses very many atoms. The wavelength of a typical photon of light is about one thousand times greater than the size of an atom. Our photon can therefore be pictured as a spread-out fuzzy ball which can encompass about one billion atoms at once ($1000 \times 1000 \times 1000$). As it proceeds through matter— quite unlike the tiny antineutrino—its exposure to the absorbing atoms is enormous. Instead of having to proceed the full ten feet to be absorbed, our photon has to go only one billionth so far, because at each instant a billion different atoms have the opportunity to absorb it. Its penetration distance is, therefore, only about 3×10^{-7} cm, or fifteen layers of atoms, quite a difference from the three thousand light-years the antineutrino travels! Typically, when we look at a solid object, we see only its outside surface because photons of visible light cannot penetrate any significant distance into it.* There are a few exceptions, such as glass and lucite, into which visible photons can penetrate many feet, but we shall not go into the special reasons for this. Even for the exceptions, it is only photons of certain wavelengths which can get very far. Ordinary glass, for example, stops ultraviolet photons in a very short distance (thereby providing protection against sunburn).

Notice in the examples above that two different factors accounted for the vast difference in how far neutrinos and photons could penetrate into solid matter. First was the difference in wavelength of the two particles. Second, and more fundamental, was the difference in exposure times required to bring about absorption. The photon needed an exposure time to atoms of 10^{-8} sec; the neu-

---

* Photons of short wavelength usually penetrate matter more deeply than photons of long wavelength because the short-wavelength photons encompass fewer atoms at each instant. Penetrating x-rays have wavelengths considerably shorter than those of visible-light photons.

trino needed an exposure time to nuclei of 10^3 sec, one hundred billion times longer. The difference in these exposure times is a reflection of a fundamental difference in interaction strengths. Because the difference is so great, physicists separate the electromagnetic interactions responsible for photon absorption and the "weak interactions" responsible for neutrino absorption into two distinct classes. (There are two other classes of interactions, which will be dealt with in Chapter Six: the gravitational, weaker than the "weak"; and the "strong," even stronger than the electromagnetic.) We have to conclude that the "weak interactions" are well named. The neutrino, which experiences only weak interactions, is practically unstoppable.

How was the antineutrino ever detected, if it can penetrate through the whole earth and through any and all experimental apparatus as if nothing were there, leaving no trace? The law of probability governing the elementary processes in nature comes to the rescue of the physicist trying to stop the antineutrino. It is true that, on the average, this elusive particle can penetrate three thousand light-years of solid matter. But some antineutrinos travel even farther than this average before being absorbed, and others are stopped sooner, a few—a very few—even within a distance of a few feet or a few centimeters. It is for this tiny fraction which "by chance" die a premature death, being absorbed in a distance much less than all the rest of their brothers, that the physicists trying to confirm the existence of the antineutrino had to look.

The experiment that definitively demonstrated the existence of the antineutrino was carried out at Savannah River, South Carolina, in 1956, by Clyde Cowan and Frederick Reines, two physicists from the Los Alamos Scientific Laboratory in New Mexico. What Savannah River had to offer them, which Los Alamos did not, was a powerful nuclear reactor, a rich source of antineutrinos. The interior of a reactor is highly radioactive, second only to a nuclear explosion in the intensity of its beta radioactivity. Within the reactor uranium nuclei are undergoing fission; that is, they break apart into lighter nuclei. These fission fragments, as they are called, are themselves almost always radioactive, after a time emitting beta particles (electrons) accompanied by antineutrinos. This radioactivity is a by-product of the fission process, having little to do directly with the operation of the reactor. The rate of production of antineutrinos within the reactor could be calculated,* as could the chance that any one of them would be stopped within the experimental apparatus. The infinitesimally small chance of catching one antineutrino multiplied by the enormous number of antineu- trinos available gave the number that should be caught in the apparatus. Reines and Cowan reckoned that they could stop one antineutrino every twenty minutes—not many, but enough.

The heart of the experimental arrangement was a sandwich of tanks, ordinary water in the three-inch-thick "meat" layer, and a special liquid called a scintillator in the two-foot-thick "bread" layers. In order to increase the chances of catching antineutrinos, the experimenters built up a "club sandwich" (Figure 5.2) taller than a man and nearly as broad and as deep as it was tall. Sur- rounding the scintillator tanks were over a hundred photoelectric cells, or "electric eyes," looking at the darkened interior of the tanks. These were connected, in turn, to a complicated array of electronic circuitry whose function was to analyze and report to the experimenters what the photo cells saw.

Whenever an energetic charged particle moves through the liquid, losing energy as it goes, the liquid gives off a weak pulse of light to signal the passage of the charged particle; that is, the liquid scintillates. Scintillators, both liquid and solid, are frequently used to detect elementary particles, but the tanks of Reines and Cowan were probably the biggest scintillators ever employed. A scintillator can also indirectly react to the passage of a neutral particle through it. A photon, for example, may be absorbed by an electron, and give to the electron enough energy so that it causes a scintillation. A neutron may be absorbed by a nucleus, stimulating the nucleus to emit radiation, which in turn gives energy to elec- trons which then provoke the scintillation pulse. In a similarly in- direct way, the capture of an antineutrino may be recorded by the scintillating liquid.

The trick is to separate and definitely identify the pulses of energy resulting from the antineutrino capture amid energy pulses arising from a variety of other elementary events continually going on in the tanks. Besides the antineutrinos, other particles—neutrons,

---

* The actual production rate of antineutrinos in the Savannah River reactor has never been officially revealed because it is directly related to the total reactor power which is a secret. However, it is certainly a very large number, probably at least 10^{18} antineutrinos per second.

gamma rays, and some charged particles, both from the reactor and from the normal cosmic radiation—are entering the tank in a steady stream, and being stopped there. The first, and easiest thing to do, is to surround the tank with a thick wall of shielding material—earth and lead blocks. This keeps out most of the unwanted

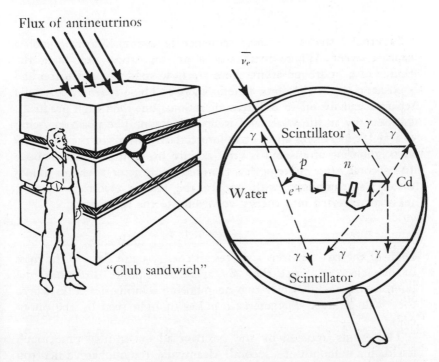

Figure 5.2. The antineutrino-detection experiment of Reines and Cowan. The "meat" in the club sandwich is a three-inch-thick layer of water (rich in protons) seasoned with cadmium chloride, because cadmium nuclei capture neutrons readily. The "bread" is a two-foot-thick tank of liquid scintillator viewed by photoelectric tubes. The chain of events set off by an antineutrino capture is described in the text.

particles, but offers no impediment at all to the antineutrinos. The second and more difficult thing to do is to discriminate electronically between antineutrino-capture events and extraneous events known as background. It is this task that required the special ingenuity of the experimenters.

Let us consider now exactly what happens on the submicroscopic scale when an antineutrino is captured. Each molecule of water in the "meat" layers contains two hydrogen atoms, and at the center of each hydrogen atom is a proton. It is the job of these protons to capture the antineutrinos through the reaction

$$\overline{\nu}_e + p \rightarrow n + e^+.$$

Figure 5.2 shows a typical sequence of events following such a capture event. Where there was a proton sitting quietly at the center of a hydrogen atom, there are now suddenly a neutron and a positron, each with some kinetic energy. These two new particles separate and fly off in different directions, but then each gradually loses energy in the water and is slowed down. The positron, being charged, experiences an electric interaction with all of the electrons in neighboring atoms and is very rapidly brought to rest (in about 10^{-9} second, after covering less than one centimeter). Almost immediately, it annihilates with one of the atomic electrons as their mass is converted into energy according to the reaction

$$e^+ + e^- \rightarrow \gamma + \gamma.$$

Each of the two photons acquires an energy equivalent to the mass of one electron. Since they fly apart in opposite directions, the photons will usually enter two neighboring scintillation tanks where they will produce characteristic pulses of light seen by the photo cells.

The events initiated by the positron all occur in a time much less than a millionth of a second. Meanwhile, the uncharged neutron is making its way through the water in more leisurely fashion, caroming off nuclei for several millionths of a second before being brought to rest (actually to a low speed, not exactly zero). Wanting to make sure that the neutron, once slowed down, is promptly captured, the experimenters added to the water some cadmium chloride, since cadmium nuclei gobble up slow neutrons with particular enthusiasm. It is for this reason that cadmium is often used in reactor "control rods" to soak up excess neutrons and prevent the nuclear reaction from getting out of hand. Following the neutron capture, the cadmium nucleus emits one or more gamma rays that fly into the scintillation tank to signal the capture event.

Altogether, then, three pulses of energy result from the capture of an antineutrino by a proton. The first two are simultaneous pulses in each of two neighboring scintillators as a pair of photons signal the annihilation of a positron. The third is a pulse of one or more photons occurring several millionths of a second later signalling the capture of a neutron. Moreover each of these three pulses has a characteristic identifying energy which the photo cells can measure—0.5 Mev for each of the annihilation photons, and about 9 Mev total for the neutron-capture photons. In 1956, five years after the first efforts to trap the antineutrino began, Reines and Cowan announced the definite observation of the electron's antineutrino through the identification of this characteristic sequence of scintillation pulses about three times per hour while the reactor was in operation.

The observation of the muon's neutrino in 1962 by a group from Columbia University required the use of a wholly different set of experimental tools. The basic capture reactions,

$$\overline{\nu}_\mu + p \rightarrow n + \mu^+ \quad \text{and} \quad \nu_\mu + n \rightarrow p + \mu^-,$$

can take place only if the neutrinos (and antineutrinos) have sufficient energy—over 100 Mev—to create the mass of a muon. The chance that the capture will occur increases as the energy of the neutrinos increases, so that a prerequisite for success in this experiment was high energy, which dictated the use of the largest available accelerator. The successful experiment was carried out at the Alternating Gradient Synchrotron at Brookhaven (Figure 1.4). Actually, for a reason to be mentioned below, the machine was operated at only 15 Bev for this experiment, about half of its maximum energy.

Via a short chain of intermediate events, the Brookhaven AGS readily provides a copious supply of high-energy neutrinos (see Figure 5.3). Energetic protons within the machine collide with nuclei in a target, producing a spray of secondary particles. Numerous among these are pions. The charged pions, as they fly from the accelerator, undergo spontaneous decay to provide the needed neutrinos, according to the transformations

$$\pi^+ \rightarrow \mu^+ + \nu_\mu \quad \text{and} \quad \pi^- \rightarrow \mu^- + \overline{\nu}_\mu.$$

Because the secondary particles must carry away from the collision the same large momentum that the high-energy protons brought

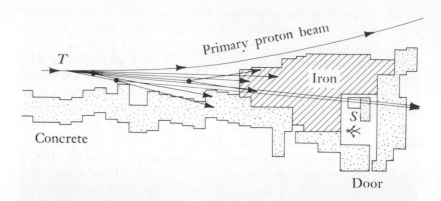

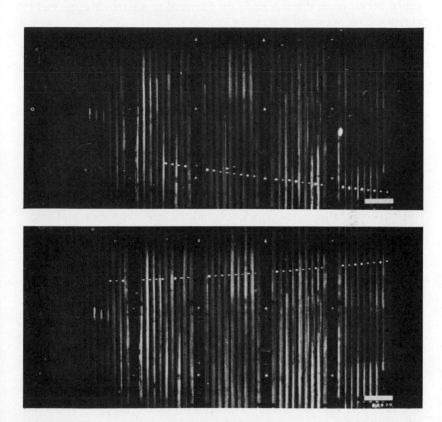

Figure 5.3. Discovery of the second neutrino. At the top of page 142, the circulating proton beam in the Brookhaven AGS strikes a target *T*; secondary particles of all kinds spray to the right. Lines penetrating 44 feet of iron and the spark chamber *S* represent neutrinos from pion decay. The iron or concrete stops almost all other particles (shorter lines). A reclining experimenter in the spark-chamber room shows the scale. (Magnets guiding the primary proton beam in its circle are not shown.) Below this is shown the 10-ton spark chamber containing 90 parallel aluminum plates, each about 4 feet square. Sparks jump between the plates to signal the passage of a charged particle. Above are two photographs of spark tracks left by muons created when neutrinos were captured in the chamber. To record 29 significant muon events, about 3×10^{17} protons were accelerated in the AGS and 10^{14} neutrinos passed through the chamber.

into it, these neutrinos and antineutrinos, along with all of the other debris from the collision, fly forward in a narrow cone rather than fanning out in all directions.

In order to get rid of unwanted particles and study the neutrinos alone, the experimenters erected, in the way of this heterogeneous beam, a solid wall of iron 44 feet thick. Behind the wall stood a spark chamber (Figure 5.3), a device in which sparks jumping between closely spaced metal plates trace the path of a high-energy charged particle. At the chosen machine energy of 15 Bev, the iron battlement was sufficient to stop all of the secondary particles except neutrinos, but to neutrinos it offered no impediment whatever. (At an operating energy of 30 Bev, 44 feet of iron would not have been quite sufficient to shield the spark chamber from all other particles.)

Coursing through the spark chamber were neutrinos and antineutrinos in large numbers, each having a chance of less than one in a million million to be caught. If the capture reaction indicated by

$$\overline{\nu}_\mu + p \rightarrow n + \mu^+$$

occurs, then, once in a while, a positive muon will be created within the chamber and leave a track. But if the muon's neutrino were the same as the electron's neutrino, the creation of positrons should also be possible, just as in the Savannah River experiment; in fact, positron creation should occur equally often. Similarly, negative muons and electrons would be created in equal numbers. In some 300 hours of operation, the Columbia-Brookhaven group observed 29 significant muon tracks in their chamber and no electron tracks. They thereby positively identified the muon's neutrino and, at the same time, showed it to be distinct from the electron's neutrino.

As this book is being written, the discovery of the second neutrino is still reverberating in the world of physics. One can only hope that the identification of still another member of the elementary-particle zoo will provide a useful further clue to the riddle of the multiplicity of particles.

If the antineutrino had *not* been detected in 1956, physicists the world over would probably still be in a state of shock. We could not easily have parted with the conservation laws of energy, momentum, and angular momentum all at one blow. But even as it was giving reassurance to scientists that these sacred laws were not being violated, the neutrino was figuring prominently in the destruction of another law—the law of parity conservation (the meaning of parity will be discussed in Chapter Eight). Here we want to mention only an unexpected new property of the neutrino that emerged from the study of parity. The neutrino is left-handed.

According to quantum mechanics, a particle such as the neutrino with one half unit of spin may have that spin directed either along the direction of the particle's motion, or opposite to the direction of motion. For example, if we imagine the earth shrunk down to elementary particle size and its rotational angular momentum reduced to one half of the quantum unit $\hbar$, then the earth could move either with its north pole leading or with its south pole leading. If the north pole is leading, an onlooker in the path of the earth sees a counterclockwise motion, and in this case the spin is said to be directed along the motion. In the opposite case, with the south pole leading, the spin is said to be directed opposite to the motion. The first case—north pole leading—is also called right-handed motion, because then the spin motion and direction of flight are combined in the same way as in the advance of a "normal" or "right-handed" screw or bolt. This can be remembered by the "right-hand rule." Let the right thumb point in the direction of flight. The fingers, if bent slightly, then indicate the direction of right-handed rotation.

An electron or a proton or a neutron—particles with one-half unit of spin—can move in either a right-handed sense or a left-handed sense, that is, with their spin motion directed along the motion or opposite to the motion. The remarkable fact discovered about the neutrino in 1957 is that it is always left-handed (and the antineutrino is always right-handed).

This left-handed character has been verified for both the electron's neutrino and the muon's neutrino. Here we mention only why the muon's neutrino is known to be left-handed. A positive pion disintegrates into a positive muon and a neutrino which fly apart energetically (Figure 5.4). Because of the conservation laws, all of the neutrino's properties can be inferred from observation of the muon alone. What is found is that all of the muons emerge with a left-handed motion, spin directed backward along the path of flight as in Figure 5.4. Now, momentum conservation implies that the neutrino flight path must be just opposite to the muon flight path. And angular-momentum conservation implies that the spin directions of muon and neutrino must also be opposite. Therefore, the neutrino must have come out with left-handed motion also. (Use the right-hand rule to check this in Figure 5.4.) Finally, the argument is turned around to say that the muon comes out left-handed in this decay *because* the neutrino is left-handed.

There is a subtlety here associated with which of the emerging particles is "really" left-handed. Suppose we board a rocket ship

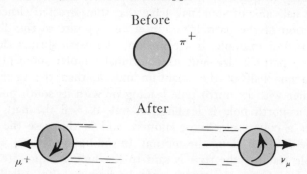

Figure 5.4. Creation of a left-handed neutrino in the decay of a positive pion.

and overtake the muon on its flight away from the point where the pion decayed. As we come abreast of the muon, we will see its "north pole" pointing toward the rear of our rocket ship, its "south pole" toward the front, just as in Figure 5.4. But if we look out of the window of the rocket ship at the muon as we pass it by, it will seem to be moving to our rear, that is, with its "north pole" leading. Relative to our rocket-ship vantage point, the muon is now right-handed. But we cannot perform the same trick on the neutrino. Because it is moving at the speed of light we cannot overtake it, and no matter how we view it, it will always appear left-handed. It is, therefore, legitimate to speak of the neutrino as a left-handed particle. The muon, on the other hand, may be in a left-handed state of motion or a right-handed state of motion, and is not intrinsically one thing or the other.

We end this section on neutrinos with a discussion of neutrinos and the cosmos—a fascinating subject because the universe is so copiously supplied with neutrinos, yet a frustrating subject because the chances of making any useful observations of these cosmic neutrinos is so slim. What do we know about the comings and goings of neutrinos on the cosmic scale? The interesting thing is that they seem to be coming, but not going. Every star is producing and supplying to the universe a steady stream of neutrinos. But so weak is the interaction of these neutrinos with the rest of the matter in the universe, that practically none of them is ever reabsorbed. Nearly every neutrino ever born in the ten to one hundred billion years that we call the age of the universe is still alive.

Within most stars, hydrogen is being converted into helium. This "burning" of hydrogen proceeds indirectly by a number of intermediate steps, but the over-all process from beginning to end can be represented in the symbolic form,

$$2e + 4p \rightarrow (nnpp)_{He} + 2\nu_e + k\gamma,$$

where the notation $(nnpp)_{He}$ means two neutrons and two protons bound together in a helium nucleus, and $k\gamma$ means an indeterminate number of photons. That this must be the net reaction follows simply from the conservation laws. Since two of the four protons are converted into neutrons, charge conservation requires that two units of negative charge be supplied to neutralize these two protons; therefore, two electrons (the only available negative particles) must participate. But electrons satisfy an electron-family conservation law; when they contribute their charge and disappear, two neutral members of the same family must appear and these must be neutrinos. Finally, energy conservation requires something extra to carry away the energy that has been generated by the hydrogen-burning process. This job falls to the photons. When the neutrinos are formed, they escape immediately unhindered from the body of the star and begin a nearly eternal journey through space. Photons, on the other hand, must fight their way to the surface of the star by a long series of absorptions and re-emissions. By the time the photon energy is radiated from the surface of the star, it has been widely dispersed; for every high-energy neutrino that leaves the star, about ten million low-energy photons are radiated. But the total stellar energy carried away by neutrinos is about ten per cent of that carried away by photons. The typical neutrino leaving the sun has an energy of about 1 Mev. The typical photon has an energy of about 2 ev, which is in the range of visible light. Note that it is only neutrinos, no antineutrinos, that the stars are pouring into the cosmos.

The fact that we can see stars some ten billion light-years away shows that photons have a good chance to travel through the universe unstopped. This means, of course, that neutrinos have an even much better chance. In fact, a rough estimate is that, in traveling across the known part of the universe for about ten billion years, a neutrino has only about one chance in 10^{25} of being captured! Our universe is quite tenuous, tiny specks of matter are scattered through the vastness of space. It falls very far short indeed of providing the solid wall three thousand light-years thick that would be required to stop a low-energy neutrino. Over the succeeding billions of years, stars will continue to pour a substantial part of their energy into swarms of neutrinos coursing about the universe in private, as it were, having no further effect on the universe. It seems exceedingly unlikely that man will be able to tap cosmic neutrinos for their energy or even for much information—for they do, in principle, carry interesting information, being the only direct messengers from the interior of stars.

Just as the earth receives most of its light, photons, from the sun, so it receives most of its neutrinos from our own sun. For every million neutrinos striking the earth, one comes from outer space and the other 999,999 come from the sun. On each square centimeter (an area about the size of a fingernail) of the earth in each second, the sun pours about 4×10^{10} (forty billion) neutrinos and about ten million times as many photons. This means that, at any instant, each cubic centimeter of volume in and near the earth contains about one neutrino. One physicist is said to have given a friend as a gift an empty matchbox labeled "Guaranteed to contain 100 neutrinos." To put the matter on a more human scale, we can say that each of us, in the time it takes to blink an eye, is struck by something over 10^{12} neutrinos.

The difficulty of observing or using solar neutrinos is put in relief simply by noting that the flux of antineutrinos which Reines and Cowan had at their disposal beneath the Savannah River reactor was about one billion times greater than the flux of solar neutrinos. An arrangement similar to theirs for catching solar neutrinos would stop one every few thousand years.

The Graviton

The graviton as a particle has not played much role in physics. The reason for this is not so much that it has never been observed —for the neutrino was an important part of the elementary-particle world well before its direct observation—as that it is not known to have any connection with the other particles or with their transformations. The graviton stands alone, being responsible for the transmission of gravitational forces among macroscopic and astronomical bodies, but having nothing to do—so far as we now know —with the elementary events of creation and annihilation occurring in the submicroscopic world. Another way to say this is that the quantum aspects of gravitation have not yet made themselves felt in any way.

It is instructive to compare gravity with electricity. We know various "classical" macroscopic aspects of electricity—currents in wires, bolts of lightning, radio and television waves. These are aspects of electricity in which the quantum aspect, or photon aspect, is entirely unimportant. Yet the quantum or photon aspect of electricity becomes of dominant importance in the atomic or nuclear world where individual photons have vastly greater energies than, say, individual radio photons. Moreover, the electrical force is what holds atoms together and is what makes uranium fissionable. Electricity spans the whole spectrum from single elementary-particle events to the large-scale macroscopic world of our senses, from the dominance of discrete particle aspects to the dominance of continuous wave aspects.

For gravity, we know only the large-scale end of this spectrum. The reason for this is quite simple. The gravitational force is extraordinarily weak, weaker by far than the "weak" interactions experienced by the neutrino. The gravitational force between an electron and a proton is smaller than the electrical force by the fantastically large factor of about 10^{40}. Small wonder that it is the electrical force that holds these particles together to form the hydrogen atom, and that when the hydrogen atom changes its energy, it does so by emitting or absorbing photons, not by emitting or absorbing gravitons. In the everyday world, the simple act of picking up a nail with a small magnet illustrates this factor of difference. The magnet (basically electrical in nature) pits its upward pulling power against the downward gravitational force of the entire earth, and easily wins the contest.

Yet, in the solar system and the galaxy, gravity, the weakest of all forces, becomes the number one pulling agent. It outstrips the strong interactions and the weak interactions because these are of short range. Although basically stronger than gravity, their effect is negligible beyond about 10^{-13} cm, and they are of no consequence in holding the solar system together. Electricity, like gravity, is a long-range force (it does get weaker as the distance increases, but it dies off very gradually compared with the rapid decrease of the short-range forces). But the sun and planets are (almost precisely) electrically neutral, made up of equal numbers of positive and negative particles. The electrical force is, therefore, cancelled out and gravity is left to dominate the scene.* The observed gravitational forces involve such an incredibly great number of gravitons that it is quite hopeless, in the foreseeable future, to imagine detecting a single graviton whose effect, in isolation, is even weaker than the effect of a neutrino.

A question frequently asked among physicists, but one whose answer no one knows, is this: Will the graviton always remain a particle apart, unconnected with elementary events in the submicroscopic world, or will it be found to "belong," contributing in some way to the deeper structure of the particles? The idealist answers that nature is in the habit of tying her separate parts together into a related whole, that it would be surprising if the graviton were not significant in the world of the very small, and that moreover, the graviton may be just what is needed to help overcome the mathematical road-blocks to progress that have appeared when theorists try to describe the particles without including the graviton in the family. The pragmatist answers that there is at present no evidence whatever that the graviton has anything to do with the transformations or the structure of the other particles, and that it is idle to speculate about that possibility now.

---

* It was mentioned earlier that the long-range forces are transmitted by massless particles—electricity by the photon, gravity by the graviton. One might think that the weak interactions ought to be long range too, because they are transmitted by the massless neutrino. The reason they are not is that the neutrino is never created or absorbed by itself, but always jointly with an electron or a muon. The weak interaction is transmitted not by the neutrino alone, but by a pair of particles, only one of which is massless.

Chapter Six

Other Particles and Strange Particles

When an electron and a positron meet, they annihilate each other. A positron and a proton approaching each other exert a mutual electrical repulsion and turn aside. A proton and a neutron are drawn together by the powerful nuclear force. A neutron and an electron (to complete the circle) are practically oblivious of one another and can coexist with scarcely any mutual interaction. Not unlike the denizens of the animal world, the members of the elementary-particle zoo interact with each other in a rich variety of ways, sometimes with attraction, sometimes with repulsion, sometimes strongly, sometimes weakly, sometimes with annihilation in mind, sometimes with a live-and-let-live attitude. About these mutual interactions we have learned a great deal in recent years—their study is the central theme in particle research—but in many important ways they remain baffling.

Every particle is, to a greater or lesser extent, gregarious. Each one reacts in some way to the presence of every other one, although that reaction may be anything from the barest nod of recognition to the explosive violence of annihilation. In fact, as we now know, events of annihilation and creation accompany every interaction, no matter how weak, but a full discussion of this new comprehensive view of particle interactions is postponed to Chapter Seven. It is better to think of interactions as slow and fast, rather than weak and strong. It is rather like comparing the friendship of a reserved Britisher with that of an open-handed western American. One friendship takes longer than the other to get started, but is just as warm in the end. A neutrino may need to traverse three thousand light years of matter to stimulate a responsive chord, but its final absorption is as total and unequivocal as the sudden death a photon finds after penetrating one millionth of a centimeter of matter. However, although annihilation and creation events *accompany* every interaction, a pair of particles may, and usually does, survive an encounter.

A particle and its interactions are inseparable; the best way to approach an understanding of the properties and behavior of the particles is through their interactions. We sometimes speak of the "intrinsic" properties of a particle, those properties which are associated with the particle alone, irrespective of how it behaves in the presence of other particles. Mass, charge, and spin are among those identifying characteristics called intrinsic. Of course, even an intrinsic property can only be discovered and measured via interactions. We know that a particle is charged because it can emit and absorb photons and exert forces on other charged particles. We measure its mass by finding out how quickly it responds to a force (an interaction) that is exerted upon it. We learn its spin only through reactions with other particles. Interactions are the glue joining the parts of the world into a coherent whole—not just in the literal sense of forces holding atoms and molecules and planetary systems together, but also as transmitters of information. Only through the elementary-particle interactions is one part of the world made aware of other parts; in particular, only through these interactions does man gain information about his environment and about the rest of the universe. As was emphasized in Chapter Five, directly or indirectly, it is the interaction of photons with charged particles that brings to man most of his knowledge as well as most of his energy.

Needless to say, a particle with no interactions at all is a nonentity. Since it has no way to make its presence felt, it is, for practical purposes, nonexistent. Every citizen of a free country may invent as many such particles as he likes, and no physicist will prosecute. Noninteracting particles are entirely harmless, and are quite outside of science. When Einstein banished the ether from science at the beginning of this century, it was because the ether had become totally noninteracting and unobservable, therefore superfluous.

Before being able to catalogue the particles and their more interesting properties in a useful way, we must catalogue their interactions. By far the most striking fact about the particle interactions is that they all belong to one or another of just four distinct and markedly different classes:

1. The strong interactions
2. The electromagnetic interactions
3. The weak interactions
4. The gravitational interactions.

We saw already in Chapter Five that the photon is associated with the electromagnetic interactions, the neutrinos with the weak interactions, and the graviton with the (still weaker) gravitational interactions. Since, for the thirty-six different particles, taken two at a time, there are 630 different pairs to interact, it is a giant step toward simplicity to discover that only four different kinds of interactions govern what goes on between all of these pairs.

Although the strong and weak interactions are imperfectly understood (as their uninspired names suggest), and though the connections, if any, among the different kinds of interaction are entirely unknown, there are some intriguing facts in hand about the four types of interaction—facts which nature dangles tantalizingly before the theoretical physicist, but which he has not yet been able to use.

First is the quite remarkable disparity of strength among the different interactions. The strong interactions exceed the gravitational interactions in strength by the fantastically large factor of about 10^{40}. The nuclear glue (strong interaction) makes the cosmic glue (gravity) look puny indeed. The electromagnetic interactions fall short of the strong interactions by a factor of "only" about 100, but exceed the weak interactions in strength by the enormous factor of 10^{13}. The weak interactions in turn are some 10^{25} times stronger than the gravitational interactions. In fact, these numbers do not have a very precise meaning, but they indicate clearly that there exist vast gulfs between the strength of one interaction and another.

The second intriguing fact about the four types of interaction is a rule which can be stated roughly: the stronger, the fewer. Of the fourteen kinds of particles listed in Table 1, eight (including all of the meson particles and baryon particles) experience strong interactions, eleven (all but the neutrinos and the graviton) experience electromagnetic interactions, thirteen (all but the graviton) experience weak interactions, and all fourteen experience gravitational interactions.* Or, turning the rule around: the weaker the interaction the larger the number of particles it embraces. Moreover, a particle that experiences any interaction in the hierarchy always experiences all weaker interactions as well; as one goes down the list to weaker interactions, names are added to the list of particles, but none is subtracted. Thus, the eight strongly interacting families of particles also experience electromagnetic, weak, and gravitational interactions. It is interesting that the heaviest eight families of particles (pions and upwards) are the ones which interact strongly. At the next rung down the ladder, the lighter muon, electron, and photon join the list. At each of the last two rungs, massless particles are added. None of these facts is understood.

Finally there is a most interesting connection between strengths of interaction and conservation laws. The seven absolute conservation laws discussed in Chapter Four govern all of the particle interactions. But, in addition to these, there are some partial conservation laws obeyed by some interactions and not by others. The rule is that the stronger the interaction, the more it is hemmed in by additional conservation laws which limit the possible transformations among the particles. The strong interactions are subject to laws of conservation of parity, of charge conjugation, of isotopic spin, and of strangeness. (What these peculiar-sounding conservation laws are all about is the subject of Chapter Eight. We are here only interested in the number of laws.) The weaker interactions then become lawbreakers, the weaker, the more lawless. The electromagnetic interactions "violate" the law of isotopic-spin conservation (in other words, electromagnetic interactions are not limited by this law). The weak interactions go further and violate all four of these special conservation laws. Since nothing is actually known of the gravitational interaction on the elementary submicroscopic level, it remains an open question whether the gravitational inter-

---

* Even the massless particles experience gravity because gravity, the most universal of the interactions, attracts any bundle of energy whether or not that energy is concentrated in the form of mass. That photons are influenced by gravity, for example, was first demonstrated by observations of the bending of starlight by the sun. In 1960 it was verified to much greater accuracy by a terrestrial experiment in which the tiny gain of energy of a photon was measured as it "fell" vertically in the earth's gravitation field.

action goes even further in lawlessness and breaks one or more of the sacred "absolute" conservation laws. If it does so, the consequences would probably be significant only in the cosmological domain. For example, violation of the law of baryon conservation by the gravitational interaction could lead to the gradual creation of new protons and neutrons, as proposed in the continuous-creation theory of the universe, or to a gradual erosion of these units of matter, undermining the material structure of the world. Fortunately we know experimentally that the latter process, if it occurs at all, is too slow to be of any consequence over hundreds of billions of years. Gravity could also be responsible for giving to space and time a nonuniform structure (as the general theory of relativity predicts that it should do), in which case it would remove the fundamental symmetry supporting the laws of energy, momentum, and angular-momentum conservation. But again, in this case, these conservation laws would be so nearly true that their failure could have significant consequences only over the vast cosmological stretches of space and time where gravity is the ruling interaction.

To proceed methodically through the list of particles, their interactions, and their properties would make a long and dull catalogue of facts, for a great deal of data has been accumulated about the particles. But among all the facts, two kinds stand out as especially interesting, and probably especially important. In surveying the particles in the remainder of this chapter we pick out only selected excerpts from the catalogue of facts that fall into one or the other of the two categories. Either they illustrate in a particularly simple and beautiful way some fundamental aspect of a law of nature or they underline clearly some important area of ignorance. The very existence of the electron as a stable particle, for example, is a fact belonging to the first group, for it illustrates the simple power of the law of charge conservation and incidentally verifies the accuracy of that law to an extremely high degree of precision. The relationships mentioned above among the strengths of interactions, the number of particles affected, and the number of conservation laws enforced are facts of the second kind. They surely must be significant and will, no doubt, one day rightly be regarded as clues that should have led physicists of today toward an understanding of the links between the different kinds of interactions. Nevertheless, they stand at present only as landmarks of ignorance on the frontier of knowledge.

Muons and Electrons

In the muon and the electron, nature has presented us with a puzzling pair of "identical" twins, exact copies of each other except that one is a giant, the other a dwarf. The muon is some two hundred times more massive than the electron, yet in almost every other way it is indistinguishable from its small brother.

Actually, the *family* of electron together with its neutrino is a twin system to the two members of the muon family. Because of the near identity of the two neutrinos, one can speak of the muon and electron separately as almost twins. Each is a negatively charged particle with a positively charged antiparticle, each has one-half unit of spin, each participates in a simple family-number conservation law, and, most important, each of these two small families seems to have precisely the same interactions with all of the other elementary particles. This is the only such pairing known in the particle world, and it is like a semaphore signal waving before the eyes of the particle physicist. But so far the message has not been read.

There must be a "reason" for the chasm between the masses of these twin particles, a reason which ought to be reflected in some other difference in their properties. So far, however, no other difference has shown up, in spite of the fact that the muon is by far the most accurately studied of the short-lived particles. Nor has any convincing theoretical explanation for the mass difference been offered. The puzzle of the muon-electron mass difference belongs to that class of questions we have learned enough to ask, but not enough to answer.

In spite of the enormous factor of difference in their masses, the muon and electron are the two lightest charged particles and they are the only two massive particles which experience no strong interactions. Although a long way apart, they are at least nearest neighbors in the catalogue of particles. All heavier particles are strongly interacting. The only lighter particles are massless.

Before examining some of the points of identity between the muon-electron twins, we must consider two questions. Why is the big discrepancy in the mass of the twins so worrisome? Why is the vast difference in the lifetimes of these two particles *not* a problem (that is, why is it not considered a real "difference" at all)?

Mass is the most highly concentrated and the most mysterious of the forms of energy. We have no deep theoretical understanding of the nature of mass, of why the proton—or any other particle—has just so much energy locked up within it in the form of mass, and not more or less. Yet, through the raw experimental data of particle masses, nature has yielded up a few clues about the origin

TABLE 3

First particle	Mass of first particle (in energy units of Mev)	Second particle	Mass of second particle (in energy units of Mev)	Mass difference between first particle and second particle (Mev)
π^+	139.6	π^-	139.6	0
π^+	139.6	π^0	135.0	4.6
K^+	493.8	π^+	139.6	354.2
K^+	493.8	K^0	498.0	−4.2
p	938.2	n	939.5	−1.3
p	938.2	K^+	493.8	444.4
p	938.2	$\bar{p}$	938.2	0
Σ^+	1189.4	Σ^0	1192.4	−3.0
Σ^+	1189.4	Σ^-	1197.1	−7.7
Σ^+	1189.4	Λ^0	1115.4	74.0
Σ^+	1189.4	$\overline{\Sigma^+}$	1189.4	0
Ξ^-	1320.8	Σ^-	1197.1	123.7

and the magnitude of masses. It is on the basis of the superficial knowledge built on these clues that the muon-electron mass difference seems paradoxical.

In order to give the reader the pleasure of seeking these clues on his own, we write down in Table 3 some masses and mass differences for a number of different particle pairs. In order not to prejudice the case, the electron and muon are omitted from the table, and the masses are expressed in terms of their equivalent energies given in Mev (million electron volts*) rather than in the electron-mass units that are used in Table 1. The point is to find clues about mass from among the heavier particles, pretending that we do not know about the electron and muon, then to apply these clues to predict roughly how big the electron and muon masses ought to be.

Inspection of Table 3 reveals, first of all, that the mass differences fall into no simple pattern. None is, say, just twice or three times another. However, the differences are interesting in one way. They fall into three groups in magnitude. Some are exactly zero. Some are "small," 1 to 7 Mev, and some are "large," 74 to 444 Mev. Moreover, closer inspection shows that a particular kind of particle pair is associated with each of these three ranges of magnitude. The three pairs in the table with no mass difference are particle-anti-particle pairs: $\pi^+ - \pi^-$, $p - \overline{p}$, and $\Sigma^+ - \overline{\Sigma^+}$. The equality of mass of particle and antiparticle is a universal rule and is, in fact, understood theoretically.

For the pairs with small mass difference, we find in the table a close kinship. Each such pair consists of particles which differ only electrically. The proton and the neutron, or the positive pion and the neutral pion, or two different Σ particles, are particles with different electric charge and slightly different mass, but otherwise identical. Proton and neutron are both baryons with spin $\frac{1}{2}$, whose strong interactions are exactly the same. Their electromagnetic interactions are obviously different because one is charged and one is not.

The natural conclusion is that the particles must have different mass "because" they have different charge, that, in some way, the electromagnetic interaction is producing the mass difference. Quantum mechanics does tell us that a particle's interactions should contribute to its mass, but does not reveal how much. The experimental evidence is that the electromagnetic contribution to mass amounts to a few Mev. It is striking that for particles as completely different in mass and in other properties as the pion and the Σ

---

* Recall that the word "electron" in the energy unit "electron volts" has nothing special to do with the electron.

particle, the electromagnetic mass differences are roughly the same. How an "interaction" can contribute to the mass of a particle that is all alone and apparently not interacting with anything else is an important question that is postponed to later in this chapter.

If the electromagnetic interactions contribute only a few Mev of the total mass, where does the rest come from? Our table also provides a hint about the answer to this question. Going on to the large mass differences, we find these between particles that differ more drastically. The real key is that these particle pairs do not have identical strong interactions. The proton and the kaon, although both strongly interacting (as is every particle in the table), do not have precisely the same strong-interaction properties. Perhaps the strong interactions are responsible for these large mass differences. This is an appealing idea and a reasonable one. The strong interactions are about one hundred times stronger than the electromagnetic interactions, and the large mass differences in the table are about one hundred times greater than the small mass differences.

Table 3 contains one more vital clue. Looking now at the particle masses themselves, not merely at their differences, we find them to lie in the range 130 to 1,300 Mev. But the large mass differences lie in the same range. A logical guess is that whatever is producing the large mass differences could, in fact, be producing practically all of the mass. This job can only fall on the shoulders of the strong interactions.

In order to appreciate the picture of particle structure to which we are led in this way, think of a builder who has at his disposal granite slabs 25 feet high, some ordinary bricks, a can of paint, and a piece of emery paper. The size of any structure he creates is determined mainly by the number of granite slabs employed. These are his "strong interaction" blocks. With one slab he builds a "pion structure," with two a "kaon structure," and with three a "nucleon structure." (Nature's big blocks are, of course, not all the same size, which complicates our task of trying to deduce the details of construction from examination of the finished product.) For slight variations of height, he can add one or two layers of bricks, his units of "electromagnetic interaction." A single slab alone might represent the neutral pion, a slab topped off with a layer of bricks the charged pion. (Again nature is not quite so simple. The addition of charge may cause a particle's mass to go either up or down slightly.) Now, for still finer control of the size of his structure he might add a few layers of paint, or whisk it once over lightly with the emery paper. His can of paint would be labeled "weak interactions," and stamped on the emery paper would appear "gravitational interactions." A light dusting with emery paper would not be likely to produce any measurable change in the size of the structure, and it is probable that the gravitational interactions contribute nothing significant to particle masses. Even the weak interactions are expected to produce only very tiny contributions to mass.

The picture of particle structure that emerges from a study of the experimental masses, mixed with some suggestions from the theory of quantum mechanics, is this. The big blocks of elementary matter are contributed by the strong interactions. Superimposed on this coarse structure is a finer structure (about 100 times finer) of bricks of matter contributed by the electromagnetic interactions. A very much finer structure (the layers of paint) which is normally negligibly small can be contributed by the weak interactions. Mass *differences* between particles arise from differences in their interactions. If their strong interactions differ, the particles differ greatly in mass. If their strong interactions are the same but the particles have different electrical interaction, they differ in mass by a much smaller amount. If the particles are the same in both strong and electromagnetic interactions, as are particle-antiparticle pairs (except for the sign of the charge, which turns out not to matter), they have no mass difference at all.

On the basis of this much understanding of particle masses, what prediction can we make about electron and muon? These are particles with no strong interactions at all. They ought to be constructed with electromagnetic bricks alone without the use of the big blocks of strong interaction. The natural prediction to make is that structures which do not interact strongly at all should have small masses and small mass differences, say, less than about 7 Mev. With the electron and neutrinos, all is well. The neutrinos are massless, and the electron mass is 0.5 Mev, even a bit less than we should happily tolerate. We may even think of the electron as just a charged neutrino. The electron and its neutrino have the same strong interaction (namely none) and differ only electrically, being in roughly the same relation to each other as the π^0 and π^- mesons. But what of the muon, with a mass of 105 Mev? It blatantly violates our hard-won rules. Its mass, not much less than that of the pion, suggests that it contains a strong-interaction block, but a number of careful tests have revealed no strong interaction whatever for the muon.

By this little excursion into the question of particle masses, we gain some insight into the reason why the muon is "anomalous." It doesn't belong. First, it violates the rule that only strongly inter-acting particles have large mass. Second, it violates the rule that particles must have different properties in order to have different masses—for electron and muon appear (so far) to have all the same properties. We can get off the hook of the second paradox just by assuming that muon and electron must have some differences which have not yet been discovered. But there is no escape from the first paradox. If a particle interacts strongly, it interacts strongly, and there is no missing the fact. No amount of careful study of a flea will convert it to an elephant. There can be no doubt; the muon does *not* interact strongly. Since we cannot escape the paradox, we must obviously have some faulty ideas about mass which need recasting. That is the present state of the dilemma. The muon, being the most bothersome particle in refusing to obey the rules, may turn out to be the particle that teaches us how to change the rules.

The second question to be disposed of was: Why is the lifetime difference not an important difference? We have the audacity to say that muon and electron are alike in every respect except mass, yet the muon lives two millionths of a second while the electron lives forever. The first thing to say about this difference is that two millionths of a second *is* practically forever. In this length of time, the muon can travel a distance some 10^{18} times its own size. To re-turn to the analogy in Chapter Two, this is comparable to an auto-mobile traveling more than 10^{15} miles (which, in fact, is farther than the total distance covered by all the automobiles ever built) before falling apart. We should not hesitate to say that such a car lived practically forever (at ten thousand miles per year, it would last one hundred billion years).

But the extremely long life of the muon on the microscopic time scale is not the main point. The key fact is that it is only "by chance" that the electron lives forever. The law of charge conserva-tion thwarts the natural inclination of the electron to end its life by transforming into lighter particles, whereas the muon can decay without violating any conservation principle and therefore does so. The difference is like that between two apparently identical toboggans, one released on the slope of a hill, one set on a flat spot part way down the same hill. The first will reach the bottom after a time, the second will never get there; the difference is not in the toboggans, but in their different starting points.

Just what is the evidence that muon and electron are "identical"? There is a large number of experimental facts which point to this conclusion and we shall mention three of them here. The first has to do with the way in which the pion decays. A positive pion, for example, may end its life in either of two ways:

$$\pi^+ \to \mu^+ + \nu_\mu$$
$$\pi^+ \to e^+ + \nu_e.$$

Out of a large number of positive pions, 99.986 per cent will transform to a positive muon plus a neutrino, and only 0.014 per cent will transform to a positron plus a neutrino. So overwhelming is the pion's preference for the muon mode of decay that, for a long time, it was believed that pions *never* decayed to electrons. Had this proved to be true, it would have been a serious blow to the "twin" theory of muon and electron. Fortunately, the infrequent electron mode of decay was discovered in 1958 to bolster the idea that electron and muon (together with their respective neutrinos) are really alike except in mass.

According to the modern form of Fermi's theory of weak interactions, the chance that a pion decays into a muon or into an electron should be proportional, among other things, to the *difference* between the speed of light and the speed of the created muon or electron; in symbols:

$$c - v,$$

where c is the speed of light and v is the speed of the muon or electron. Now, the muon created in the usual mode of pion decay is rather speedy. It flies away from its point of creation at about one seventh of the speed of light. But if the pion had chosen to decay into an electron instead, this much lighter particle would have acquired a far greater speed, in fact more than 99 per cent of the speed of light. The *difference* $c - v$ is, therefore, very much smaller for the swift electron than for the heavier more sluggish muon. As a consequence, the chance of pion-to-electron decay is much smaller than the chance of pion-to-muon decay.

It can be regarded as merely a mathematical quirk of the theory of weak interactions that the pion happens to prefer to decay into a heavier slower particle rather than a lighter speedier one. The important point is that this mathematical quirk accounts perfectly for the observed preponderance of pion-to-muon decays, and no difference at all between muon and electron aside from their mass is needed to account for the big difference in the two ways a pion may decay. Until the tiny, but significant, fraction of pion-to-electron decays was discovered it looked as though muon and electron showed a "real" difference. Moreover, the principle that nature does everything not forbidden to her by a conservation law was saved from an unexplained exception.

One of the chief functions of electrons is building atoms. A hydrogen atom contains one electron, a helium atom two, and so on up past the uranium atom with its 92 electrons. If muons and electrons are basically the same, then it should be possible to build atoms with muons as well as with electrons. This is quite true, but the job is not so easy. The physicist trying to do some atom-building with muons is like an artist trying to complete a painting using paints that fade into invisibility after one second. Before he could apply a second color, the first would have vanished. Still, if he worked like lightning, he might complete some very rudimentary paintings in a single color. The physicist, working literally like lightning—in times of a millionth of a second or less—can build some simple muon atoms and study them for an instant before the decay of the muon terminates their existence. These muon atoms have provided some valuable data supporting the twin theory of muon and electron.

The problem is getting enough muons in the same place at the same time. If a beam of muons strikes a target material, a particular atom in the target may capture a muon and begin the process of converting itself from an electron atom into a muon atom. But before it can catch a second muon, the first will have vanished. So far, the physicist has had to be content with single-muon atoms, like the artist with monochromatic paintings. Even these provide useful information.

An important fact about a muon atom is that it is about two hundred times smaller than an electron atom. This comes about because of two aspects of the wave nature of matter discussed in preceding chapters. The first is the de Broglie wavelength relation, which says that more momentum means shorter wavelength. A muon stands in the same relation to an electron as a freight car to an automobile. At the same speed, the heavier object has more momentum. Since muon and electron have about the same speed within an atom, the muon has a much greater momentum and much shorter wavelength. The second fact is simply that the size of an atom is determined by the wavelength of its electrons (or muons). A particle can not be forced into a region of space shorter than its own wavelength. So when a muon attaches itself to an ordinary atom, it cascades into ever smaller orbits, soon coming within the innermost electron orbit, until finally it falls down to its own lowest state of motion, circling the nucleus in a tiny orbit two hundred times closer than the nearest electron.

As the muon jumps successively to lower orbits on its journey toward the nucleus, it emits photons whose study has yielded information about the muon—especially the precise value of its mass —as well as some information about the shape and size of the nucleus at the center of the atom.

Once lodged in its lowest orbit (which it reaches in much less than a millionth of a second), the muon may do what it would have done anyway, that is, decay into an electron, a neutrino, and an antineutrino, which fly away at high speed. But it has another course of action open to it, a course it follows more readily the larger the nucleus to which it is attached. The muon may combine with one of the protons in the nucleus to produce a neutron and a neutrino:

$$\mu^- + p \rightarrow n + \nu_\mu.$$

This reaction conforms to all of the conservation laws and releases considerable energy—about 100 Mev. Some of this energy is carried off by the neutrino; the rest goes into disrupting the nucleus. For a few artificially produced radioactive atoms, a similar process of electron capture occurs, in which one of the inner electrons is gobbled up by the nucleus, a proton is transformed into a neutron, and an electron's neutrino is released. (This is, incidentally, the most harmless variety of radioactivity. The only particle shot out of the atom is a neutrino, which can harm no one.) Comparisons of the muon-capture process and the electron-capture process have provided more evidence that muon and electron differ only in mass. They are otherwise captured in exactly the same way.

By far the most impressive demonstration of the equivalence of electrons and muons has come from the measurements of the intrinsic magnetism of these particles. As most schoolboys know, a

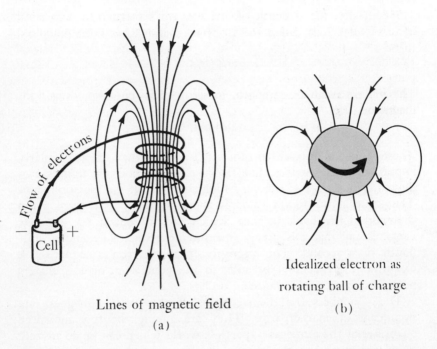

Lines of magnetic field

(a)

Idealized electron as rotating ball of charge

(b)

Figure 6.1. A macroscopic magnet and a microscopic magnet. Both derive their magnetism from the circulation or rotation of electric charge.

wire wound round and round an iron nail and connected to a dry cell produces a respectable little electromagnet (Figure 6.1). The circulation of electrons flowing around the coil of wire produces a magnetic field (which the iron nail helps to magnify). As far as we know, *all* magnetism is produced in basically this way—by the rotational or circulating motion of electric charge. The idea is as good on the submicroscopic level as on the macroscopic level, and as good for a single elementary particle as for a wire and an iron nail. Every charged particle that is spinning, for example, the electron or the muon, represents electric charge in rotational motion, and every such particle is, therefore, a tiny electromagnet. Modern techniques of measurement have made it possible to determine the strengths of these one-particle magnets with phenomenal accuracy.

Specifically, the strength of the electron's magnetism, expressed in terms of a unit called the Bohr magneton,* has been measured to be

$$1.0011596.$$

The muon's magnetic strength, in terms of its corresponding Bohr magneton, is

$$1.001162.$$

These numbers are written down not because they are particularly important in themselves, but because the number of figures employed is indicative of the very high accuracy of the measurements. The error in the muon value is about the same as that of a ten thousand dollar bank balance which fails to check by just five cents. Recall that this precise measurement was made in one millionth of a second. The strength of an electron's magnetism is measured more accurately still, to the equivalent of less than a penny in one-hundred thousand dollars.

These numbers for the strengths of the particle magnets are significant in another way. They are among the few measured quantities of the elementary-particle world which can be accurately calculated from theory—that is, which are "understood." Dirac's quantum theory of the electron (1928) has been joined with Maxwell's theory of electromagnetism and the theory of photons to give a theory of the electric and magnetic properties of electrons (and, apparently, of muons as well) which bears the formidable name of quantum electrodynamics. Mathematical difficulties beset

---

* The Bohr magneton is $eh/4\pi mc$, the elementary unit of charge multiplied by Planck's constant h, and divided by 4π times the mass of the particle times the speed of light. This happens to be a convenient unit because it is equal to the strength of magnetism a particle would possess if it obeyed simply the classical laws of electromagnetism and had one unit of spin.

this theory for twenty years, and were only cleared away around 1948.* It then became possible to calculate the theoretically expected values of the electron's magnetic strength,

$$1.0011596;$$

and, assuming it differs from the electron only in mass, of the muon's magnetic strength,

$$1.001165.$$

Within the limits of experimental error these values agree with those which have been measured. Because of the high precision of the measurements, this constitutes an excellent test of the idea that the muon and the electron are twins.

The reason such accurate values of magnetic strength can be calculated for these particles is that muon and electron have no strong interactions, and the weak interactions have no appreciable effect on the magnetism of the particles. Only the electromagnetic interactions play a role and, of the four classes of interactions, these are the best understood.

Most physicists are tantalized by the muon-electron puzzle. We know so much about their similarities, but so little about the reason for their vastly different masses. Nature is trying to tell us something through these two particles free of all the complexities of strong interactions, but we do not know what. In the words of Abdus Salam,† one of the leading theoretical physicists interested in these problems: "I believe [our present theories] are but stepping-stones to an inner harmony, a deep pervading symmetry. The muon may seem out of place today. When we discover its real nature we shall marvel how neatly it fits into the Great Scheme, how integral a part it is of something deeper, more profound, more transcending. Faith in the inner harmony of nature has paid dividends in the past. I am confident it will continue to do so in the future."

---

* Actually, quantum electrodynamics still contains some mathematical puzzles. What happened in 1948 was that enough of the mathematical roadblocks to progress were cleared away to permit accurate calculation of some electron and muon properties. But the theory as a whole still has some troubling features. It is unlikely to survive the next few decades in its present form.

† In *Endeavour*, April 1958.

Pions and Nucleons

The pion has the distinction of being one of the only particles for which the theorist got there first. Most of the particles have been discovered first, and "explained," if at all, later. But Yukawa predicted the existence of the pion more than ten years before its discovery.

When the proton, known since early in the century, was joined in 1932 by the neutron, physicists immediately realized that atomic nuclei must be built up of protons and neutrons. We now know that these two particles, together known as nucleons, have more in common than being the bricks of nuclear matter. They have very nearly the same mass, and seem to behave identically in all respects, except electrically, standing roughly in the same relation to each other as the positive and neutral pion, or as the electron and its neutrino. Stated simply, the proton is nothing but a charged neutron (or the neutron an uncharged proton).

The discovery of strong interactions can be said to have co-incided with the discovery of the neutron, for as soon as the view of nuclei as aggregates of nucleons emerged, it was clear that there must exist a new kind of force—the nuclear force—with two important properties: It must be considerably stronger than the electrical force (for it could hold protons together within the nucleus in spite of their electrical repulsion); it also must act only over very short distances, not more than 10^{-12} cm (for nuclei were no larger than this, and their effect upon passing particles extended no farther than this). It was mainly to explain the second fact, the short range of the strong interactions, that Yukawa, in 1935, postulated the existence of the pion, a particle whose exchange among the nucleons was supposed to provide the nuclear glue.

We must now grapple with a very important idea in contemporary thinking about the submicroscopic world, the idea of a "virtual particle." This idea provides a very beautiful example of the workings of the Heisenberg uncertainty principle at the elementary level, and will provide a clue, not only to the nature of the strong interactions, but to the nature of *all* forces and interactions.

In the form in which it was written down in Chapter Three, the Heisenberg uncertainty principle looked like this:

$$\Delta x \Delta p = \hbar.$$

The uncertainty in the position of a particle (Δx) multiplied by the uncertainty in its momentum (Δp) is equal to the constant $\hbar$. Now, in fact, this fundamental uncertainty in nature arising from the wave nature of particles manifests itself in more ways than in the measurability of position and momentum. Another form of the same basic uncertainty in nature can be written:

$$\Delta t \Delta E = \hbar.$$

The uncertainty of time (Δt) multiplied by the uncertainty of energy (ΔE) is also equal to the constant $\hbar$. This means a precise measurement of energy (small ΔE) requires a long time (large Δt). Or if an event occurs at a very precisely known time (small Δt), its energy cannot be accurately determined (large ΔE). Never can time and energy both be precisely known at once. In particular, tests of the law of energy conservation require processes extending over some time.

That these two different forms of the uncertainty principle both occur is not surprising when we recall that, according to the theory of relativity, space and time are closely linked, as are energy and momentum. The origin of both forms of the law is the wave nature of matter. Just as a wave cannot be localized in a region of space smaller than its own wavelength, so it cannot be pinpointed in a time interval shorter than one period of its vibration. The only way to squeeze a wave more in space is to shorten its wavelength; the only way to squeeze it more in time is to shorten its period, that is, make it vibrate faster. But the higher the rate of vibration, the higher the energy. Thus, a more precisely defined time must go with greater energy. Turning to music, the only way to get a pure tone, free of harmonic overtones, is to let the note vibrate through many cycles of oscillation. Similarly, the only way to get a "pure" energy, precisely defined without uncertainty, is to let the particle wave vibrate many times, that is, to allow a large span of time, or a large uncertainty of time. The wave picture of matter leads in a simple way to the time-energy uncertainty as it led to the position-momentum uncertainty.

Before applying this new form of the uncertainty principle to the nuclear force, we shall jump ahead and learn one fact about the relation of pions to nucleons. A typical process of pion creation in an accelerator may be written symbolically in the form,

$$p + p \rightarrow p + n + \pi^+.$$

A high-energy proton strikes a proton at rest in a target, and from the collision emerge a proton, a neutron, and a positive pion. The simplest interpretation of this event is to say that one of the protons breaks up into a neutron and a pion,

$$p \to n + \pi^+.$$

This process obeys all the conservation laws but one—energy. The masses of neutron and pion add up to considerably more than the proton mass, so that a single free proton left to itself would never decay in this way; to do so, it would need to violate energy conservation. But when it is struck by another energetic proton, some of the energy of motion in the collision can be converted to mass energy and the process becomes allowed. The extra needed energy is made available in the collision. Our picture of the event is something like this. A proton "wants" to convert into a neutron and a positive pion. The strong interaction between nucleons and pions makes such a transformation always a possibility. But the transformation cannot be realized unless some extra energy is supplied. The proton is like a car parked on a hill; the law of energy conservation is the parking brake holding it back. In a high-energy collision, the energy is supplied to release the brake and the proton can follow its natural inclination for change.

Yukawa did not know these facts about pion production but he surmised them. His further reasoning, reduced to nonmathematical terms, continued somewhat as follows: Although energy conservation prevents such a transformation as

$$p \to n + \pi^+$$

from occurring as a definite and irrevocable step, the uncertainty principle introduces into the law of energy conservation a kind of leniency which permits such a transformation to occur as a transitory phenomenon. We might say that the policeman enforcing the law of energy conservation is willing to look the other way if the violation lasts a short enough time. The pion may dart briefly outside the walls of its nucleon prison, and in again, before any enforcement procedures are initiated.

The talk of leniency and enforcement has to do simply with the uncertainty principle:

$$\Delta t \Delta E = \hbar.$$

If we want to "violate" the law of energy conservation, that is, introduce into the energy an uncertainty of amount ΔE, we may do so provided the time of violation, Δt, is no longer than that set by this uncertainty relation. Now the numerical value of $\hbar$ is $\hbar = 7 \times 10^{-22}$ Mev-sec. The excess energy needed for a proton to convert into a neutron and a pion is roughly the energy equivalent of the pion mass, or 140 Mev. The allowed time duration of this much energy uncertainty is

$$\Delta t = \hbar / \Delta E.$$

Dividing the numerical value of $\hbar$ by the numerical value of ΔE gives the time uncertainty, $\Delta t = 5 \times 10^{-24}$ sec, a very short time indeed! How far could the temporarily freed pion move in this time? Traveling as fast as possible (at nearly the speed of light) it would only cover 1.5×10^{-13} cm.

According to Yukawa, then, instead of being merely a dead sort of object, sitting quiescent, the proton is, even when all alone, in a constant state of activity. It may eject and then immediately (after 5×10^{-24} sec) recall a positive pion,

$$p \leftrightarrow n + \pi^+.$$

The double arrows indicate the two-way nature of the process. Or it may eject and recall a neutral pion,

$$p \leftrightarrow p + \pi^0.$$

Because the interaction responsible for this activity is strong, these processes occur repeatedly and the proton must be regarded as a center of continual activity. The pions which come into momentary existence are called "virtual" pions. They are not "real" pions because energy conservation prevents their escape and they can never dart away to leave a track in a cloud chamber or otherwise be observed. Nevertheless, the success of Yukawa's theory is enough to make us believe in this picture of the proton. Like a chauffeur on the sidewalk of Fifth Avenue surrounded by a barely controllable group of French poodles on leashes, the proton is surrounded by its cloud of virtual pions, darting this way and that, but leashed by the uncertainty principle to remain within little more than 10^{-13} cm of the nucleon core.

This picture of the proton has received strong support in recent years by a series of "electron scattering" experiments carried out at Stanford University by Robert Hofstadter.* Electrons of several hundred Mev energy are fired at targets containing protons. Some of these electrons pass "through" the protons, that is, through the cloud of virtual pions surrounding the proton cores. In doing so, they are deflected, some through a small angle, a few through large angles. Detailed study of the fraction of electrons emerging in each direction reveals something about the size and composition of the pion cloud. The virtual pions do extend to a bit more than 10^{-13} cm, as our calculation above with the uncertainty principle indicated that they should. The average penetration of a pion away from the nucleon core is about eight tenths of a fermi, 0.8×10^{-13} cm. (Actually, the proton cloud contains some kaons and a few other kinds of particles, but consists mostly of pions.)

The final step in Yukawa's line of reasoning had to do with the force between two nucleons. All that the uncertainty principle requires is that each virtual pion in the cloud surrounding the proton must vanish almost immediately after it is created, to clear the books of this excess mass energy. If a nucleon stands alone, the pion must be reabsorbed by the same nucleon from which it emerged. But if two nucleons are close together, a pion could be emitted by one and absorbed by the other. Suppose, for example, that a neutron approaches close to a proton. At a particular instant, the proton may have transformed itself momentarily into a neutron and a positive pion. The other neutron can absorb the pion to become, itself, a proton. The net result is that a pion has jumped across from proton to neutron and, in the process, proton and neutron have changed roles. Yukawa realized that this kind of pion exchange could produce a strong attractive force between the two nucleons, a force now called an exchange force. Within a nucleus, virtual pions have to be thought of as constantly coming and going, frequently being exchanged back and forth between the nucleons. It is this incessant juggling with pions (and, to a lesser extent, with kaons) that provides the nuclear glue holding neutrons and protons together.

Because he knew roughly the range of the nuclear force, Yukawa

---

*For his work on the structure of nucleons, Hofstadter received the Nobel prize in physics in 1961 (which he shared with Rudolph Mössbauer, the discoverer of a technique which made possible the measurement of the influence of gravity on photons mentioned on page 154).

was able to predict approximately the mass of a pion. The more massive a virtual particle, the more seriously it strains the law of energy conservation, therefore the more briefly it is permitted to exist. Since it can move no faster than light, the shorter-lived virtual particle will penetrate less far from its parent particle and create a tighter, smaller cloud. A second nucleon, in order to feel the exchange force from the first, must come up to the edge of the cloud of virtual particles. The range of the force is, therefore, about the same as the size of the cloud. Virtual particles heavier than pions would produce an even shorter-ranged force. Virtual particles lighter than pions would produce a longer-ranged force.

The concept of the transitory creation of virtual particles helps to explain an idea introduced near the beginning of this chapter —the idea that the mass of an isolated particle arises from "interactions," even though there is no other particle in its vicinity to interact with it. In fact no particle, even if alone, is ever quiescent. It is always "interacting," for it is always creating and annihilating its own cloud of virtual particles. This process of self-interaction contributes to the particle's own mass, for the particle obviously represents a localized bundle of energy, which is nothing other than mass. The particles that interact strongly, pions and all heavier particles, presumably have the most intense clouds of virtual particles and correspondingly the most self-energy, or mass. The particles that do not interact strongly, the muon and lighter particles, have less self-interaction and less mass.

In spite of this degree of qualitative understanding of mass, however, the picture is far from satisfactory. For one thing, it has so far proved impossible to deduce theoretically the mass of any particle. Moreover, according to some theories, a stronger self-interaction should produce a greater *decrease* of mass, in contradiction with experiment. Also, as already emphasized, the muon mass does not fit into even the qualitative pattern. The problem of elementary-particle masses is obviously far from solved.

A final fact about nucleons needs to be discussed briefly, not because it illustrates any new ideas or points to areas of ignorance, but because of its enormous practical significance. This is the stabilization of the neutron. If a neutron were not stabilized in the presence of one or more protons, the world would have not 92 elements occurring naturally but just one, hydrogen. A neutron alone undergoes the beta decay process, transforming to proton, electron, and antineutrino after an average time of seventeen minutes. Joined to a proton, it can acquire an infinite lifetime, making possible the building of all the elements heavier than hydrogen. If this were not the case, all of our elements would long since have decayed into the lightest element, hydrogen.

What stabilizes the neutron is a rather peculiar "chance," that the pion exchange force between a neutron and proton happens to be somewhat stronger than the same force acting between two protons. The nucleus of deuterium, or heavy hydrogen, consists of one proton and one neutron. The mass of this combination (the deuteron) is not simply the mass of a proton plus the mass of a neutron, but somewhat less than this sum. The attractive force that pulled neutron and proton together has released energy and this lost energy, called the "binding energy," is reflected in a decreased mass of the deuteron. Now, the neutron in the deuteron has a natural inclination to undergo beta decay. This is normally a "downhill" process, for the neutron transforms to a lighter proton. If the deuteron's neutron decides to follow this inclination, the deuteron becomes suddenly a pair of protons. But these protons are held together less tightly than the neutron-proton combination; they have less binding energy. The gain in going from heavier neutron to lighter proton is more than offset by the loss of binding energy. The law of energy conservation therefore prevents the neutron decay. The neutron is stabilized by the energy binding it to the proton. This is all a very delicate balance, the stabilization of the neutron amounting to less than one part in a thousand of the neutron mass. Yet we have reason to be grateful for this rather strange combination of circumstances—that the neutron happens to be so little heavier than the proton, that the pions happen to hold neutron and proton together more tightly than two protons. Viewed in terms of our present knowledge of elementary-particle interactions, it is a remarkable miracle that nature has some ·90 atomic building blocks available instead of just one.

Strange Particles

In 1947 the list of known particles (counting one of the neutrinos as "known," but omitting the graviton) stood at fourteen. The most energetic accelerator in the world pushed protons to about 200 Mev. Cosmic rays remained the principal source of high-energy particles for experimental study, and the cloud chamber was the chief tool of elementary-particle research. Just eight years later the list of particles had jumped to thirty. The Berkeley Bevatron had been completed to accelerate protons to 6,000 Mev (6 Bev). The center of gravity of particle research had shifted from cosmic rays to accelerating machines, and the bubble chamber, a vital new tool of particle research, had been invented.

The sixteen new particles that appeared on the scene during these revolutionary eight years belonged to the four families, kaons, lambdas, sigmas, and xis. All were unpredicted, unexpected, and "strange." Physicists shrugged their shoulders in wonder and mentally braced themselves for the discovery of more and more particles. But the flood subsided as abruptly as it had begun. Nine years passed before the next strongly interacting long-lived particle, the omega, was discovered in 1964.* Thanks to a scheme of classification discovered independently in 1953 by two young physicists, Murray Gell-Mann in America (then aged 23) and Kazuhiko Nishijima in Japan (then 26), there is some reason to think that very few, if any, more will be found.

The new particles first made themselves known through some unexplained V-shaped tracks in the cloud chamber of George Rochester and C. C. Butler of the University of Manchester. A more recent picture of such V tracks is shown in Figure 6.2. The track of an incoming pion stops abruptly in the chamber and, separated from it by a few centimeters, are two V's, each with its vertex pointing toward the end of the incoming pion track (point *A* in the figure). Measurement of momentum of the visible tracks makes it possible to infer that two neutral particles were created at point *A* and that these decayed at points *B* and *C* into pairs of oppositely charged particles whose visible tracks gave the V's.

Typically, magnetic fields are applied to bubble chambers and cloud chambers to cause moving charged particles to be deflected and leave curved tracks. In Figure 6.2, the negative particles moving to the left bend upward, the positive particles bend downward. A high-momentum particle such as the incoming pion on the right

---

* It is more accurate to say that no more strongly interacting *families* of long-lived particles were discovered in this period, for some of the individual members of the older families, such as the neutral xi, and the antilambda, have only been positively identified in recent years.

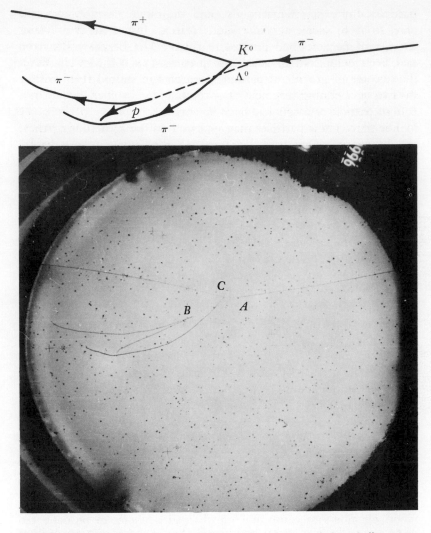

Figure 6.2. Examples of V-shaped tracks characteristic of "strange-particle" decays. At *B*, a neutral lambda decays into a proton and a negative pion. At *C*, a neutral kaon decays into oppositely charged pions. At point *A*, a negative pion entering the chamber from the right struck a proton in the bubble chamber and produced the two strange particles according to the reaction,

$$\pi^- + p \rightarrow \Lambda^0 + K^0.$$

is deviated only slightly from a straight course. A lower-momentum particle such as the negative pion from the kaon decay is more strongly deflected. By measuring the curvature of the tracks, the experimenter can determine the momentum of each charged particle. Because of the law of momentum conservation, he can then deduce the momentum of unseen neutral particles.

Immediately following the 1947 discovery of V particles at Manchester, similar tracks were noticed by other experimenters, and it was not long before the properties of these new particles were being pinned down by careful measurements in a number of laboratories. We now know that among the first V particles observed were neutral kaons and lambdas such as those in Figure 6.2, which were decaying according to the schemes:

$$K^0 \rightarrow \pi^+ + \pi^-,$$
$$\Lambda^0 \rightarrow p + \pi^-.$$

Within a few years, their charged brothers had been identified and the sigma and xi particles had been added to the roster. (For the characteristic open-V track of a negative xi, look back to Figure 1.8.)

The study of the new particles had not proceeded very far before something peculiar about them appeared. In spite of the fact that they had gone unnoticed during many years of cloud-chamber studies, they were, in fact, not particularly rare. In very energetic nuclear collisions, the chance of creating one of the new particles was appreciable, so great that there was no escape from the conclusion that the new particles must interact strongly, like the pions and nucleons. Particles which experience only electromagnetic and/or weak interactions could not be produced as frequently as the new particles. Expressed in terms of a time, one of the new particles could be produced after only about 10^{-22} sec if enough energy were available. Yet, once produced, they lived a million million times longer than that, about 10^{-10} sec. That, said the physicists, is very strange. And the new particles became the "strange particles."

The long life of a pion or a muon is understandable because it decays into particles which interact only weakly. But, in the decay of a lambda, for example,

$$\Lambda^0 \rightarrow p + \pi^-,$$

the products of the decay—proton and pion—are both strongly interacting particles, and so is the lambda itself, as proved by the ease with which it can be created. It was very hard to see what kept the lambda alive so long, why it did not take advantage of the strong interactions to convert itself immediately into proton and pion.

What makes the electron live forever is the law of charge conservation. What makes the proton live forever is the law of baryon conservation. Suppose, said Gell-Mann and Nishijima, that there is another conservation law, a new one, which makes the lambda live "almost forever." Some new physical quantity, some new "thing," has to be held constant, or conserved. The tongue-in-cheek name given to the new conserved quantity is "strangeness."

According to Gell-Mann and Nishijima, each of the particles has to carry a "strangeness number," just as it carries an electric charge, or a muon-family number, or a baryon number. The pion, eta, and nucleon are not strange; they have zero strangeness number. The lambda and the sigma are assigned strangeness number -1 (and their antiparticles $+1$). The kaon is given strangeness number $+1$, the xi, strangeness number -2, and the omega, strangeness number -3 (their antiparticles being opposite in sign).

It all sounds rather fanciful, but it works! In the absence of any deeper knowledge, the strangeness assignments are as good a guide as we have to the nature of the strange particles. Now, the conservation law is this: In every strong interaction process, the total strangeness is conserved.

In a pion-production process, such as

$$p + p \rightarrow p + n + \pi^+,$$

the new conservation law is satisfied, for the total strangeness number is zero before the collision and zero afterwards. But what if a strange particle is produced? This can be managed only if at least *two* strange particles are produced together, with opposite signs for their strangeness numbers. A typical allowed process is

$$p + p \rightarrow p + \Lambda^0 + K^+.$$

The strangeness of the two colliding protons is zero. The strangeness numbers -1 and $+1$ for the lambda and kaon cancel to conserve the total of zero. This phenomenon, christened "associated production" was proposed first by Abraham Pais shortly before the strangeness scheme of Gell-Mann and Nishijima. There is now ample experimental evidence that strange particles are always produced two (or more) at once. This was not noticed at first because one member of the pair frequently escaped the cloud chamber undetected, leaving only one to be seen. Figure 6.2 provides a

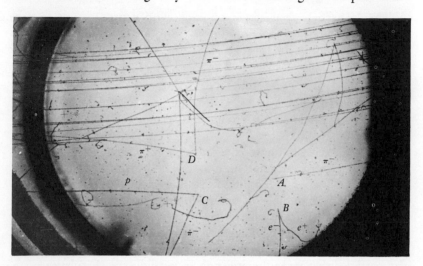

Figure 6.3. Associated production of a sigma and a kaon. At point A, a negative pion, incident from the right, collides with a proton and produces two strange particles, a neutral sigma and a neutral kaon, according to the reaction

$$\pi^- + p \rightarrow \Sigma^0 + K^0.$$

The sigma particle lives too short a time to move a measurable distance away from the point A, decaying almost at once into a lambda and a photon ($\Sigma^0 \rightarrow \Lambda^0 + \gamma$). The photon moves downward to produce an electron-positron pair at point B. The neutral lambda and neutral kaon decay with characteristic V-shaped tracks at points C and D. A few of the many other negative pions flying through the chamber from right to left also stimulate particle transformations.

good example of associated production, and another interesting example is shown in Figure 6.3.

A xi particle, with a strangeness number of -2, is usually produced with two other strange particles, for example, with two kaons,

$$p + p \rightarrow \Xi^0 + p + K^0 + K^+.$$

If a strange particle strikes a nucleon, again the strangeness-conservation law dictates what may happen. A typical allowed process is

$$\Lambda^0 + p \rightarrow n + p + \overline{K^0}.$$

A lambda particle vanishes in collision with a proton, but to preserve the total strangeness number of -1, another strange particle must be formed, in this case an antikaon. In Figure 1.8, the reaction

$$\overline{K^+} + p \rightarrow K^+ + \Xi^-$$

was illustrated. Test this for strangeness conservation (recalling that the antiparticle $\overline{K^+}$ has charge and strangeness opposite to those of the K^+).

As these examples show, the concept of strangeness constitutes more than a feeble attempt at humor. The power of this new conservation law, as of every conservation law, lies in what it forbids. There are a vast number of strong-interaction processes which are forbidden only by the conservation of strangeness; none of them has ever been detected. There can be no doubt that strangeness, whatever its deeper meaning might be, is an important attribute of the particles that strongly limits their possible transformations.

What does strangeness conservation have to say about strange-particle decay? As the simplest example, consider the kaon. It is the lightest strange particle (as the electron is the lightest charged particle, and the proton is the lightest baryon). If strangeness conservation were an absolute law, the kaon could not decay at all, and would join the ranks of the stable particles. But since strangeness conservation governs only the strong interactions, but not the weak, the kaon is only inhibited from undergoing the very speedy decay (after about 10^{-22} sec) which would characterize the strong interactions. Since the weak interactions violate strangeness conservations, they act in their own leisurely fashion and bring about the kaon decay after about 10^{-10} sec.

Strangeness conservation is just one of several new partial conservation laws (the others will be discussed in Chapter Eight) that apply to the strong interactions but not to the weak. Why some conservation laws are absolute and others partial; why strong interactions are hemmed in by more conservation laws than are weak interactions, are questions to which no one knows the answers. They remain important challenges for the future, and it seems likely that, without answers to these, no deep understanding of the particles will be possible.

Resonances

The 1950's were the era of the strange particles. The 1960's are ushering in the era of a new breed of particles so short-lived that they may not deserve to be called particles at all. For technical reasons, which are too complicated to discuss here, the super-short-lived particles are called "resonances." Our knowledge of resonances is still very fragmentary, but some things are known about them. It is known that there are quite a few, that some are strange and some are not, some are baryons and some are not, and *all* are strongly interacting. Table 4 summarizes what is known of the resonances (in 1964), but the contents of the table, and probably its length, will undoubtedly change considerably in the coming years. Even the names are mere stopgap designations which will probably be revised.

The main thing the resonances have taught us is that the thirty-five particles listed in Table 1 (not counting the graviton) are far from the end of the story. Those thirty-five are merely the particles which, for one reason or another—usually the inhibiting influence of a conservation law—live a relatively long time. The resonances round out the picture. They are the particles which interact strongly and are not prevented by any conservation law from following their natural inclination for very rapid decay. Hence, in the characteristic short time of strong interactions, they vanish and give way to lighter particles.

A typical resonance is born and dies all within a space considerably smaller than a single atom. That it ever existed can only be inferred by studies of the longer-lived products of its decay. Suppose, for example, that a proton and antiproton annihilate to create five pions,

$$\bar{p} + p \rightarrow \pi^+ + \pi^+ + \pi^- + \pi^- + \pi^0.$$

This process is illustrated in Figure 6.4. The bubble-chamber photograph shows the tracks of the incoming antiproton and the tracks of the four charged pions, apparently all emerging from exactly the same point. Energy and momentum conservation require that

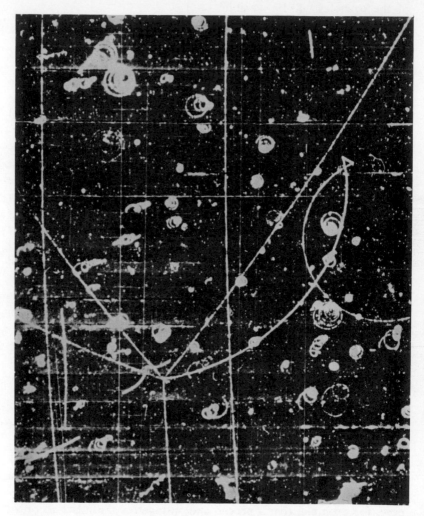

Figure 6.4. Production of an eta "resonance." The antiproton entering from the bottom annihilates with a proton in the bubble chamber
to form two pions and an eta-one particle. After a time of about 10^{-22}
sec, the eta-one decays into three more pions. The transitory existence
of the eta-one is inferred only from studies of the pion tracks. (Notice
that one of the positive pions is also observed to undergo decay into a
muon through the reaction, $\pi^+ \rightarrow \mu^+ + \nu_\mu$, and the muon, in turn, decays
into a positron according to $\mu^+ \rightarrow e^+ + \nu_e + \overline{\nu}_\mu$. The neutrinos are of
course unseen.)

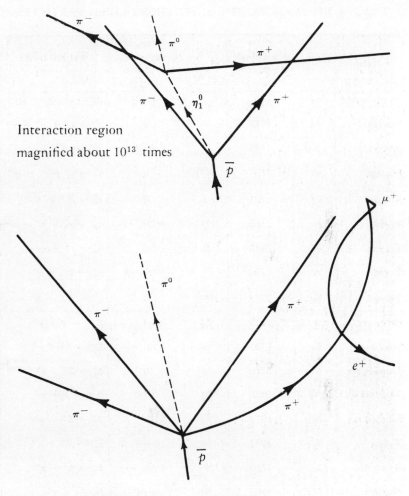

Interaction region
magnified about 10^{13} times

Figure 6.4 (Continued).

one unseen neutral pion also flew from this point. Study of many such events shows that groups of these pions tend to come off in a certain relation to each other, which implies that they must be the decay products of a single particle. This correlation of the final pions shows that what actually happens (some of the time) is a two-stage process in which, first, an eta-one particle is created,

$$\bar{p} + p \rightarrow \eta_1^0 + \pi^+ + \pi^-;$$

TABLE 4. RESONANCES, THE SUPER-SHORT-LIVED PARTICLES

Name	Symbol	Mass (in units of the electron mass)	Spin (in units of $\hbar$)	Charge (in units of proton charge)	Typical mode of decay
Pi resonance	π_1	1490	1	$+1, 0, -1$	$\pi_1^+ \to \pi^+ + \pi^0$
Eta res.	η_1	1532	1	0	$\eta_1^0 \to \pi^+ + \pi^- + \pi^0$
Kaon res.	K_1	1744	1	$+1, 0$	$K_1^+ \to K^+ + \pi^0$
Eta res.	η_2	1877	0(?)	0	$\eta_2^0 \to \eta^0 + \pi^+ + \pi^-$
Eta res.	η_3	1995	1	0	$\eta_3^0 \to K^+ + \overline{K^+}$
Pi res.	π_2	2380	1(?)	$+1, 0, -1$	$\pi_2^- \to \eta_1^0 + \pi^-$
Eta res.	η_4	2450	2	0	$\eta_4^0 \to \pi^+ + \pi^-$
Pi res.	π_3	2560	2	$+1, 0, -1$	$\pi_3^+ \to \pi_1^+ + \pi^0$
Eta res.	η_5	2760	0(?)	0	$\eta_5^0 \to K_1^+ + \overline{K^+}$
Delta res.	Δ	2420	$3/2$	$+2, +1, 0, -1$	$\Delta^{++} \to p + \pi^+$
Sigma res.	Σ_1	2705	$3/2$	$+1, 0, -1$	$\Sigma_1^+ \to \Lambda^0 + \pi^+$
Lambda res.	Λ_1	2750	$1/2$	0	$\Lambda_1^0 \to \Sigma^0 + \pi^0$
Nucleon res.	N_1	2970	$3/2$	$+1, 0$	$N_1^+ \to p + \pi^0$
Lambda res.	Λ_2	2972	$3/2$	0	$\Lambda_2^0 \to \Sigma^+ + \pi^-$
Xi res.	Ξ_1	2992	$3/2$	$0, -1$	$\Xi_1^- \to \Xi^- + \pi^0$
Sigma res.	Σ_2	3250	?	$+1, 0, -1$	$\Sigma_2^0 \to \Lambda^0 + \pi^0$
Nucleon res.	N_2	3303	$5/2$	$+1, 0$	$N_2^+ \to n + \pi^+$
Sigma res.	Σ_3	3450	$5/2$	$+1, 0, -1$	$\Sigma_3^+ \to p + \overline{K^0}$
Xi res.	Ξ_2	3540	?	$0, -1$	$\Xi_2^0 \to \Xi_1^0 + \pi^0$
Lambda res.	Λ_3	3552	$5/2$	0	$\Lambda_3^0 \to n + \overline{K^0}$
Delta res.	Δ_1	3765	$7/2$	$+2, +1, 0, -1$	$\Delta_1^- \to n + \pi^-$
Nucleon res.	N_3	4290	$9/2$	$+1, 0$	$N_3^0 \to \Lambda^0 + K^0$
Delta res.	Δ_2	4620	$11/2$	$+2, +1, 0, -1$	$\Delta_2^{++} \to p + \pi^+$

and then the eta-one decays,

$$\eta_1^0 \rightarrow \pi^+ + \pi^- + \pi^0.$$

There is no doubt that the eta-one existed as an independent entity, even though it had no time to move a measurable distance away from the point of its creation.

The resonances may be thought of as perched precariously on the upper rungs of a set of ladders. On the bottom rung of most ladders is a long-lived particle, stabilized or partially stabilized by a conservation law, or by the fact that it has no strong interactions, or by the fact that it is massless and is already as low as it can get. On the bottom rung of one ladder is the pion, the lightest strongly interacting particle. Above the pion are the several pion resonance particles, which can tumble rapidly down to the level of the pion. At the foot of another ladder is the proton, the lightest baryon. Occupying rungs above it are the short-lived nucleon resonances, N_1, N_2, N_3. On the lowest rung of still another ladder is the lightest strange baryon, the lambda. Up the lambda ladder are various strange resonances, the Λ_1, Λ_2, and Λ_3 particles.

Table 4 contains 23 kinds of resonances, or 86 different particles if all charges and antiparticles are counted separately. The number is almost sure to increase.

The big lesson of the resonances, if it was not obvious before, is that there is not a muon problem, and a pion problem, and a kaon problem. There is just one problem, the particle problem. There are far too many particles and far too many intricate interconnections among them to imagine that any one or a few particles will be understood until they are all understood.

The Magnetic Pole

We end this chapter with some remarks on a particle that has never been seen, and may very well not exist—the isolated elementary magnetic pole. There is no known rule which says it *should* exist; on the other hand, the fact that there is no known law which should forbid its existence has kept physicists wondering about this particle and sporadically searching for it for the past thirty years.

In the phenomena of electricity and magnetism, nature exhibits a remarkable asymmetry. Electric charge, the seat of electric fields and electric forces, exists in quantized lumps in the form of elementary particles. According to the theory of electromagnetism, there could very well also exist equally primitive sources of magnetic phenomena, elementary magnetic poles. Indeed the mathematical theory would have a more symmetric and pleasing form if poles as well as charges existed. But man cannot legislate for nature. Charges have been found in abundance; poles have never been found.

All magnetic phenomena appear so far to arise from the *motion* of charges. Charges alone are quite sufficient to produce both electricity and magnetism, but they do so in an unsymmetric fashion. Charge must be in motion to generate magnetism (a current in a wire, or a rotating electron), but charge alone, even if stationary, can generate electricity. A pole at rest, on the other hand, could generate magnetism; a moving pole would generate electricity. Thus poles bring a better balance to electricity and magnetism. (The poles of a bar magnet, or the poles of the earth, have nothing to do with the elementary-particle poles of this discussion.)

In 1962, several new attempts were made to detect the magnetic pole. Physicists in Geneva, Switzerland, and in Brookhaven, New York, sought poles in the debris from very high-energy proton-nucleus collisions at their respective 30 Bev accelerators. A different kind of search was carried out by a group from the Massachusetts Institute of Technology. They carried an exceedingly powerful electromagnet to regions of iron ore deposit in the Adirondack Mountains and sought to lure poles from the ore. If poles had arrived in past millenia in the cosmic radiation or had been created by cosmic-ray bombardment of the air, they should have been trapped in the earth's naturally magnetic iron ores. The result of all three experiments: no poles.

The principle that nature at the submicroscopic level does everything not absolutely forbidden to her by a conservation law has too often proved right in the past to be lightly abandoned. Most physicists, reflecting on the unseen poles, admit only two possibilities. Either there is an undiscovered conservation law that explains why poles do not exist, or poles *do* exist, but have, so far, escaped detection.

Chapter Seven

Fields and Particles, Forces and Interactions

This chapter is concerned with two of the most basic ideas in modern science. The first is the idea of a quantum field, the elemental stuff of the universe from which particles and the material world are constructed. The second is the idea of an elementary event, an explosive happening at a single point in space and time. The first is an idea of being; the second, an idea of action. From the tenuous being of fields arise the solid, lasting structures of the world. From the catastrophic action of annihilation and creation arise the smooth and orderly flow of events in our large-scale world.

Both of these ideas have been touched upon in Chapter Three. Here, we want to examine how these two ideas, together with the accumulated data supplied by the elementary particles, have shaped the scientist's view of the submicroscopic world. How has this strangely chaotic and almost incredible picture of the world of the very small evolved, and how can it be reconciled with the very different picture of the world provided by our direct sense experience?

The idea of a field was evolved by Faraday and Maxwell in England over a hundred years ago. The field entered the house of science by the back door, for to Faraday and Maxwell it stood not for any independent entity, but for a disturbed state of something else—the ether. When we speak of an ocean wave or a sound wave, we understand that the wave is a name for a particular kind of disturbed state of the water or the air, it is not really something in itself. In a similar way, when Faraday and Maxwell spoke of an electric field they pictured a disturbance—a state of strain, or non-uniformity—in the underlying all-pervading ether that was supposed to fill space. The field was a more general idea than a wave. It did not need to be vibrating or traveling. A motionless electric charge could create a stationary disturbance in its own neighborhood, called the electrostatic field. If the charge happened to be vibrating, it created an oscillating electromagnetic field which propagated through space as electromagnetic waves. It was the study of these field waves that led Maxwell to his explanation of the nature of light.

According to the Faraday-Maxwell view of fields, an electric charge isolated in an ether-filled space is like a fish in the depths of a quiet ocean. Although surrounded by water, the fish is uninfluenced by the water (or would be, if he could glide without friction through it). When another charge is introduced near the first one, the ether is "strained"; the particle feels the "field" established in its own neighborhood and is pushed or pulled, much as the fish might be affected by a depth-bomb explosion not far away. He would think he was pushed by something quite real—which he might decide to call a field—even though it is only the water that was there all along that is doing the pushing.

However, the Faraday-Maxwell field was a bit more than a name. Even though the mental image made the ether basic and the field auxiliary, in fact, the field could be defined mathematically and used in the equations of electromagnetic theory, for it was only the field, the nonuniformity in the ether, that was measurable, not the underlying ether itself.

When Einstein rejected the ether altogether as unobservable, and therefore meaningless, there was no upset in electromagnetic field theory. The mental image of the field underwent a revolution, but the equations of the theory remained absolutely unchanged. The revolution of the *picture*, however, was all-important in establishing the psychological climate for the further progress of field theory. The field for Einstein became a real physical entity, a thing, existing in otherwise truly empty space.

As a rough analogy, we can say that the idea of the field as a disturbance in a fluid was replaced by the idea of the field as itself a fluid—but not an all-pervasive one, rather one scattered about here and there, some places intense, some places thin, and frequently traveling through space in bundles of wave motion. Space became comparable to a dry creek bed in the west rather than to the depths of a calm ocean; an electromagnetic wave, like a sudden spring freshet flowing down the creek bed, instead of like a wave of pressure traveling through the sea. An electric charge absorbing electromagnetic radiation was to be thought of as an idle prairie dog in the creek bed suddenly struck by a wall of water instead of as a fish in the sea struck by a pulse of pressure.

The recognition of fields as real physical entities was the first of two big revolutions in the physicists' understanding of the field. The second was the change from the "classical" view of a field, as a fluidlike substance distributed smoothly through a region of space, to the "quantum" view of a field, as something slightly particle-like which could be created and destroyed in lumps.

Strangely enough, Albert Einstein made a vital contribution to each of these revolutions in the picture of a field. The first—the banishing of the ether and the emergence of the field as a real physical entity—was associated with his development of the theory of relativity. The second—the picture of a quantum or particle-like field—received its strongest support from Einstein's suggestion of the photon as an explanation of the peculiarities of the photo-electric effect. He discovered that electrons must absorb electro-magnetic radiation, not gradually and smoothly, but abruptly in lumps and that radiation must be emitted in the same way. The photon picture required that the field be created, not like a stream of water pouring from a hose, but like the rattle of bullets from a machine gun. This particlelike behavior is emphasized only during acts of emission and absorption. In between, the field has to be pic-tured more like the stream of water than like the bullets, a fluidlike substance, not concentrated at points, but spread out over a region of space and propagating as a wave from one point to another. Moreover, and this is all-important to the apparent smoothness and continuity of our large-scale world, a wavelike behavior is also induced even in the acts of emission and absorption when a suf-ficient multitude of bullets act in consort. We are already quite accustomed to the idea that the apparent smoothness and divisibility of ordinary matter is illusory, coming about only because of the minute size of atoms and the vast number of them in any sample of material that can be seen by the eye, or even with a microscope. To this idea of indivisible units of *matter* must now be added the idea of indivisible units of *action*. Just as apparently smooth matter is really granular at the submicroscopic level, so an apparently smooth flow of events is really an uneven, jerky succession of tiny explosions. Almost without exception, all of the smoothness and continuity we observe, in happenings as well as in material, is the result of the superposition of a vast array of elementary units.

The dual nature of the field, as both wave and particle, is something that simply defies visualization because it bears no resemblance to anything we know in the large-scale world. In spite of the limitations of our imagination, the successful mathematics of the quantum theory has forced us to this picture of wave fields which can come into and go out of existence with explosive suddenness. In order to get a rough understanding of photon absorption, imagine a film of the geyser "Old Faithful" run backward. One would see a plume of water (the "field") spread out in the air, which quite suddenly collapses and vanishes into a small hole in the ground (the "absorbing electron"). For the quantum field, such collapse of the wave occurs instantaneously, not merely quickly.

This view of the quantum field and the wave-particle duality began with the electromagnetic field and the photon in 1905. But not until the late 20's and early 30's did our present more general view of fields as the basic stuff of the universe emerge. As late as 1926, when the new quantum theory was developed, particles and fields were regarded as two different things. The dropping of the last barrier between particles and fields was forced on the physicists rather unexpectedly when they tried to merge the theories of relativity and quantum mechanics. It just turned out—for mathematical reasons which no one had foreseen—that this merger could be effected only if *all* particles, material as well as immaterial (electrons as well as photons), were regarded as the quantum lumps of an underlying field. Thus it became suddenly necessary to add to the electromagnetic field an electron field and a proton field and, as more and more particles were discovered, more and more distinct fields. The essential feature of this field theory of particles was that all particles, and not just photons, must be capable of being created and annihilated. Of course, we are now up against an embarrassing richness of fields which no one really believes in. It seems certain that each of the known particles cannot be the quantum manifestation of a distinct underlying field, but that, in some way not yet understood, all of the particles must arise from one or very few basic fields. (This view is at the moment an article of faith, not of evidence.)

To summarize the modern view of fields and particles: There is a nebulous physical substance called a field which can propagate as a wave through space and can carry energy and momentum and mass (and charge and other measurable quantities). Whenever any part of a field comes into or goes out of existence, it does so with catastrophic suddenness at a particular point of space and time. A peculiarity of every field is that it has a definite mass associated with it. A lump of electron field can be created with any kinetic energy or any momentum, but has always the same invariable mass, which is just the mass of the particle we call an electron. The two biggest mysteries of field theory today are the apparent multiplicity of different fields, and the origin of the mass carried by the field. For reasons no one knows, some fields lock up a great deal of energy in the form of mass, others very little, and others none at all.

We are going to be concerned in the remainder of this chapter with the creation and annihilation of fields, that is, with the particle-like aspects of the fields. The interaction of one field with another —the source of all the action and events in the world—emphasizes the particle properties of fields and is, therefore, easy to visualize. It will be possible to speak of, and think of, a particle being created at one point, flying somewhere else, and then being annihilated. Yet in the back of our minds should be the more complex picture of a lump of field being created, propagating elsewhere as a wave, and then being again absorbed all at once.

It is necessary first to make an excursion into some four-dimensional geography. In picturing the interactions of particles it is important to think of the when as well as the where, hence to think of paths through time as well as paths in space. This is not as difficult as it sounds. Think first of an ordinary map, say, with a vertical north-south line and a horizontal east-west line. We can draw space paths on such a map. Figure 7.1 shows the curved track followed on an auto trip from Boston to New York, the straight track of an airplane flight from Ghent to Boston and (on an enlarged scale) the circular path of electrons in the Cambridge Electron Accelerator. This space map is fine for showing routes, but does not reveal *when* the auto or the airplane or the electron was at any particular point. The nearest we can come to indicating time is attaching arrows to the routes which at least show which part of the route was earlier in time, which part later.

If. we wanted to know the routes very precisely, and not merely have a top view of them, it would be necessary to go to a three-dimensional map that revealed the airplane's altitude as well as its position over the ground. This becomes complicated. To go still further and diagram not only the airplane's position but the history in time of its flight, it would be necessary to make a four-dimensional map, which we cannot even visualize much less construct. Fortunately, just as the two-dimensional space map is very helpful, even though not exact, a two-dimensional space-time map can serve as a very useful substitute for the four-dimensional map.

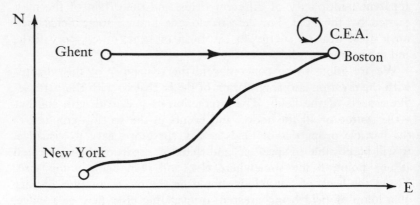

Figure 7.1. Trajectories on a space map.

Suppose, for example, that we want to be able to draw the history of the airplane flight in time as well as in space. Since it traveled due east we can dispense with the north-south line and replace it with a time line. The new space-time map will look like Figure 7.2. The horizontal direction is called x and represents distance. The vertical direction is called t and represents time. The first thing to notice is that there is no such thing as standing still in a space-time map. Something that remains at rest—the city of Ghent—still moves through time. It traces out a straight vertical line in our map; its position x is always the same, but as time moves forward it moves vertically upward in the diagram, leaving a trace that is called its "world line." The world line of Ghent is shown by a vertical dashed line in the figure, and another vertical dashed line farther east is the world line of Boston. Now what about the airplane? While parked on the field of Ghent, it also moves only through time, not through space, and also traces out a vertical world line (the segment *AB* in the diagram). Then the plane takes off and flies east, moving both in space and time, and tracing out the world line *BC*. Having landed at Boston, it once again moves only in time, and its world line continues upward.

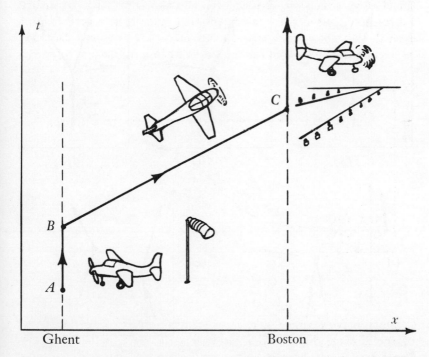

Figure 7.2. Trajectory in a space-time map.

We have attached arrows to the world line of the airplane. They may seem redundant, since there is, after all, only one possible direction to move through time—forward. But they do no harm and will serve a useful purpose in the elementary-particle world.

This simple space-time map only describes motion along a single straight line, but that will be sufficient for understanding particle interactions. We may always think of more complicated maps with, say, two space dimensions and one time dimension, but it is better to restrict the diagrams to the form illustrated here.

Turning now to the particle world, we sketch the world lines of a few simple occurrences (Figure 7.3). The first one, for example, shows the process of photon emission by an atom. Initially (starting at the bottom of the diagram) an atom is at rest and, like the city of Boston, traces out a straight vertical world line.

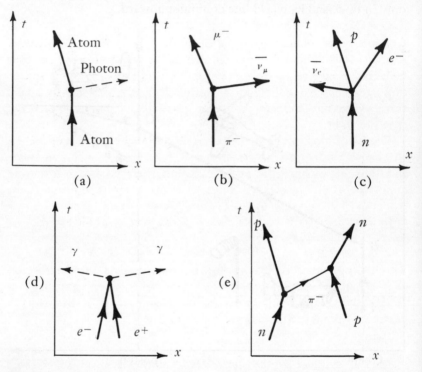

Figure 7.3. World lines of various occurrences in the particle world. (a) Emission of photon by an atom. (b) Pion decay. (c) Beta decay of a neutron. (d) Positron-electron annihilation. (e) Pion exchange process.

It then emits a photon that flies off to the right, and the atom itself, having fired the photon, recoils and moves off more slowly to the left. Notice that the more slowly a particle moves, the more nearly vertical is its world line—no motion at all is exactly vertical. Conversely, the faster the particle moves, the more its world line is tipped over toward the horizontal. But it can never become exactly horizontal; for that, the particle would have to travel from one place to another in no time at all. The photon line is tipped the maximum possible amount, for the photon moves at nature's greatest speed, the speed of light.

The next diagram, 7.3(b), illustrates pion decay,

$$\pi^- \rightarrow \mu^- + \overline{\nu_\mu}.$$

At some point, indicated by the black dot, the negative pion ceases to exist. It is annihilated and its world line terminates. But at that same place and same time (that is, at that same point in space-time) the negative muon and the antineutrino are born and fly apart, the antineutrino line being tipped at the angle corresponding to the speed of light.

The black dot locates what, in relativity theory, is simply called an "event," a happening, an occurrence, at a single point in space and time. In each of the other diagrams there is also at least one important event. In the world of particles, every significant event is marked by the creation and/or annihilation of particles.

In diagram 7.3(c) the beta decay of the neutron is illustrated,

$$n \rightarrow p + e^- + \overline{\nu_e}.$$

This time, the crucial event in space-time involves the destruction of one particle and the creation of three others. The next diagram 7.3(d) shows the annihilation of an electron and a positron to create two photons (gamma rays),

$$e^- + e^+ \rightarrow \gamma + \gamma.$$

Finally, diagram 7.3(e) illustrates a pion-exchange process that contributes to the force between a neutron and a proton. Initially (bottom of diagram) a neutron and a proton are present. They exchange a pion, and exchange roles, emerging with different speeds. According to the Yukawa theory, the force between two nucleons arises entirely from this exchange process, together with various more complicated exchanges that can also take place.

Before we go on to the question of how these pictures are related to what is "really" going on at the submicroscopic level, one flag of warning must be raised. It is possible, indeed probable, that some of the single "events" indicated by the black dots are really complex sequences of events which all happen within such a tiny domain of space and a short span of time that they only seem to be events at one single space-time point. It is already known, for example, that the phenomenon of electron-positron annihilation does not proceed exactly as pictured in diagram 7.3(d). Rather, the two photons actually emerge from slightly different points, as in Figure 7.4.

We must be prepared for the possibility that the future will reveal an inner structure to other apparently simple events, even for the possibility that the apparently catastrophic acts of sudden annihilation and creation are really the result of a smooth, continuous flow of events over tinier regions of space and time

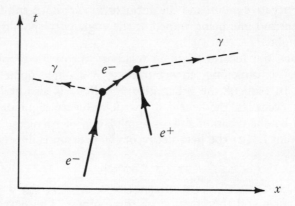

Figure 7.4. What "really" happens in a positron-electron annihilation process, a corrected version of Figure 7.3(d).

than it has been possible to investigate so far. This is pure speculation. Down to the shortest distances (10^{-14} cm) and shortest times (10^{-24} sec) to which man has probed, the elementary events of the particle world still seem to be the catastrophic events of sudden creation and destruction of the packets of field energy we call particles.

The accumulated evidence from experiments probing the world of the very small, together with the confirming support of the quantum theory of fields, leads to the following very important general conclusion: All of the interactions in nature arise from acts of annihilation and creation of particles at definite points in space and time. There are two important ideas here: First, all interactions involve the creation and annihilation of particles; second, these creations and annihilations do not take place over a region of space nor over a span of time, but are instantaneous and localized at points. By an "interaction" is meant simply the influence of anything on anything else. Thus, all ordinary forces, pushes or pulls of one thing on another, are interactions. Also, the decay of an unstable particle is the manifestation of an interaction. The final particles are "influenced" by the initial particle—they come into existence only because the initial particle was there.

Contrast this new view of interactions with the classical view. The sun and the earth "interact," for the earth is pulled by the

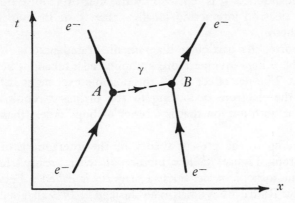

Figure 7.5. World-line diagram for the mutual interaction and deflection of two electrons.

sun. Nothing is apparently being created or destroyed, and nothing seems to be happening instantaneously at isolated points of space or time. But, according to the new view, gravitons are constantly being emitted and absorbed, both by the sun and by the earth. Each act of emission or absorption occurs at an instant of time and a point in space. The "force" the earth experiences is nothing but the accumulated effect of all of these graviton interactions.

To turn to an example in the particle world that is more surely understood, consider the "scattering" of two electrons. According to the old view, the electrons approach each other, feel a mutual repulsive force, and are slowed down and deflected. The new view gives a picture more complete, as well as different; it explains "why" the electrons exert a force on each other. In Figure 7.5 we see two electrons approaching one another. At point A, the electron on the left emits a photon and changes its speed. At point B, the electron on the right absorbs the photon and changes *its* speed. The two electrons have interacted, or exerted a force on each other, since their motion was altered. It was the exchange of a photon that brought about this apparent interaction. Strictly speaking, the basic interaction was not between the two electrons at all, but between each electron and a photon. The second electron is only indirectly aware of the presence of the first. The old idea of action at a distance, of a force "reaching out" from one to the other, is completely abandoned. It is replaced by the idea of a "local interaction," of each electron interacting locally—that is, at its own location—with a photon.

Of course, the particular diagram illustrated here is only one of many; the others involve more complicated exchanges between the electrons. The net effect of all the possible exchanges is the deflection of the electrons according to the ordinary repulsive electric force, but with motion that is a series of hops rather than a smooth flow.

According to the present theory of the interactions of electrons and photons, Figure 7.5 is a picture of what "really" happens on the submicroscopic scale. Such a diagram is called a Feynman diagram after Richard Feynman who showed in 1949 that such pictures have an exact correspondence to mathematical expressions in the field theory of electrons and photons. These diagrams, therefore, portray what is "really" happening, and provide a convenient way to catalogue the various possible processes of creation, annihilation, and exchange.

The key points of a Feynman diagram are the "vertices," representing those points at which (in this example) photons are created or absorbed. *All* processes involving photons, and therefore *all* of the interactions associated with electromagnetism, arise from elementary events of photon creation or photon annihilation. These fundamental interaction events can be pictured by a single kind of vertex that looks like either of the diagrams in Figure 7.6. The solid lines represent charged particles and the dashed line represents a photon. The points A and B in Figure 7.5 are vertices of this kind.

If the solid lines represent the world lines of electrons, for example, it appears that the fundamental interaction event may be regarded as an event in which a photon is created or absorbed, and an electron simultaneously changes its state of motion. There is, however, a more general and a more fruitful interpretation. The vertex may be taken to represent a point where the world line of one electron terminates and the world line of another begins. According to this view, the vertex represents a truly catastrophic event. Nothing survives it. Instead of thinking of a single electron being changed at the vertex, one can think of one electron being destroyed and another electron being created. Since all electrons are indistinguishable, it has no real meaning to say that the outgoing electron is the same as or different from the incoming electron. To think of the outgoing electron as a new and different

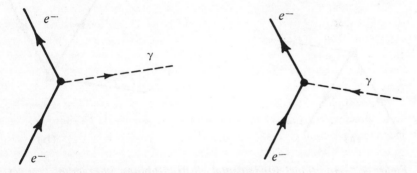

Figure 7.6. Basic electron-photon interaction vertices.

electron, however, corresponds more closely to the mathematical theory of the fundamental interaction. The creation-destruction interpretation also leads to a simple, unified description of particle events and antiparticle events.

The vertex on the right in Figure 7.4 seems to differ from those in Figures 7.5 and 7.6. Instead of being a point where one electron world line ends and another begins this vertex is a point where both an electron world line and a positron world line end. There is a simple artistic trick by which we can change the picture significantly. Suppose we turn around the arrow on the positron line. The arrowhead was, after all, redundant, since all particles move forward in time. We can use it instead as a label to distinguish particles from antiparticles. An arrowhead pointing in the "right" direction will indicate a particle (for example, an electron); an arrowhead pointing in the "wrong" direction will indicate an antiparticle (a positron). Using this revised notation, we show in Figure 7.7(a) an electron-positron annihilation vertex, and in Figure 7.7(b) an electron-positron creation vertex. Now these vertex diagrams involving positrons look like twisted versions of the fundamental vertex diagrams in Figure 7.6. The generalized conclusion is that the fundamental electron-photon vertex with its limbs twisted in all possible directions in space-time represents all the possible basic interactions among electrons, positrons, and photons. This

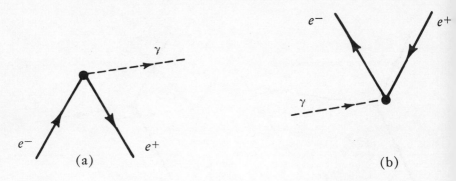

Figure 7.7. Additional fundamental electron-photon interaction vertices which include antiparticles (positrons).

provides a magnificently simple and general view of the underlying basis of all electromagnetic phenomena.

What Feynman showed when he discussed the connection between such world-line diagrams and the structure of the mathematical theory of the electron-positron-photon interaction was that the device of the reversed arrowhead is much more than an artistic trick. According to the field theory of electrons, the creation of a positron is "equivalent" to the annihilation of an electron (they are not identical processes, but the theory says that whenever one can happen, the other must also be able to happen). Moreover, the mathematical description of a positron field propagating forward in time is identical with the description of an electron field propagating backward in time. It is perfectly possible and consistent to think of particles moving backward in time as well as forward.

This circumstance need not lead us to deep philosophical conclusions, although philosophical implications are hard to escape. The positron *may* be described as an electron moving backward in time but it does not *have* to be so described. An alternative description is equally possible in which the positron is a normal particle moving forward in time. Nevertheless, this picture of backward motion in time is a tantalizing one that simplifies the view of elementary interactions and provides a "natural explanation" for the existence of antimatter. Consider the Feynman diagram in Figure 7.8, for example. According to the normal view of time unrolling one direction, we start at the bottom of the diagram and

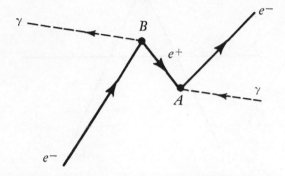

Figure 7.8. Feynman diagram for the process of photon-electron scattering.

read up. First an electron and a photon are approaching each other. At vertex A, the photon creates an electron-positron pair. The new electron flies away, while the positron collides with the first electron at vertex B. There they undergo mutual annihilation and a new photon is born.* The alternative view, which Feynman showed to be also consistent, is to picture the first electron proceeding to point B, where it emits a photon and reverses its path through time. It "then" travels to point A where it absorbs the incoming photon and once again reverses its course through time, flying off in the "right" direction. Either view is permissible and logically consistent.

---

* This process is electron-photon "scattering," known as the Compton effect. The deflection of photons by collision with electrons was discovered by Arthur Compton in 1923.

In thinking of the philosophical consequences of this remarkable view of motion in both directions through time, we must ask: What about man? Why do we move only forward through time, not enjoying the same freedom the particles have? The answer is that we *do* enjoy the same freedom, but fortunately are prevented from exercising it by a chance. Man is composed of particles, not antiparticles; particles always move forward in time. By chance (?), our corner of the universe is constructed almost exclusively from particles and contains very few antiparticles. (Whether there exist other parts of the universe where antiparticles dominate is unknown.) Therefore we cannot find the antimatter with which to

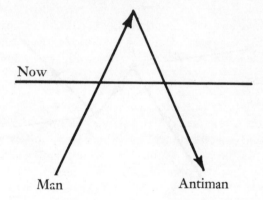

Figure 7.9. "Feynman diagram" for a man who reversed his course through time.

annihilate and start our path backward in time. Of course, an occasional positron enters every man and destroys one of his electrons, but we can always spare a few electrons.

This answer may seem unsatisfying, for the question could be phrased somewhat differently. One might ask, must the antimatter already be present? Could man not emit a barrage of photons and reverse his course in time as the electron did? The answer is that if a man were going to do this in the future, he would know it already. We are aware of what is around us *now*, and a path that later on reversed itself in time would again pass through the present *now*. In the Feynman diagram of Figure 7.9, the present moment, "now," is indicated by a straight horizontal line. If the world line of a man were to reverse, then the man and the "later" antiman would both be present side by side at this moment of time. Even if there is a science-fiction ring about it, this argument is perfectly sound and really does not differ from the argument of the preceding paragraph. Because we see no significant quantity of antimatter around us now, we can be sure that we are safe from future annihilation or time reversal.

According to the theory of relativity, there is nothing special about one direction of time. It is, in fact, satisfying to know that particles may have the same freedom to move forward and backward in time that they have to move left and right or up and down in space. This view of the world restores the symmetry of space and time and attributes the *apparent* one-way flow of time to the fact that we happen to live in a world with an enormous disparity between the number of particles and the number of antiparticles.

Unfortunately, no one knows how to test the theory of time-reversed trajectories experimentally. It must be accepted (if at all) for the symmetry it introduces into our picture of the world and for the simplicity it introduces into the description of antiparticles. To see that the direction of motion through time cannot be measured, imagine yourself a submicroscopic observer of the scene depicted in Figure 7.8. If you put a ruler horizontally across the bottom of the diagram and then push it slowly upward across the diagram, the intersections of the world line with the moving ruler edge give a rough history of your observations. (Actually the ruler should be slightly tilted to take account of the fact that signals received from other points take some time to arrive, but this is an unimportant detail for this discussion.) The point is that it is the ruler edge of your observation which is moving in time, not the world lines themselves. The particle world lines may be regarded as perfectly static, simply *there*, painted in space-time like lines on a map. To a creature capable of comprehending the whole span of time as we comprehend the span of space, the activity of annihilation and creation represented in this diagram is not activity at all. It is a stationary display, a picture painted in space and time. It is the fact that man, the observer, can comprehend only one instant of time at each moment that converts the stationary display into motion and activity. At one time, the human observer sees an electron in one place. At a later time, he sees it at a different place. It is natural for him to believe that the electron, like the man, has moved forward in time to get from the first place to the second place. But there is no essential reason to believe this. We know only that the electron world line has traced out a certain path in space-time, but we have no possible way of knowing in what order the points of that path were traced out, nor even whether it makes sense to speak of an order or a direction of tracing the world line.

These considerations lead to philosophical problems outside the scope of this book. According to the theory of relativity, forward and backward motion in time are equally acceptable and the best pictures of world lines may in fact be static lines in a four-dimensional geography. Quantum field theory has added the insight that the simplest description of antiparticles is in terms of particles moving backward through time (an idea which can also be blended with the static picture). We are still faced with the fact that man certainly moves through time in only one direction. We remember the past and do not remember the future. It is human memory *and nothing else* that tells us in which direction we move through time. Man experiences an asymmetry of time he does not share with the elementary particles. Can man's asymmetry of time be reconciled with the particles' symmetry of time if man is nothing but a collection of particles? Can man mold the course of future history if world lines are really fixed features of a four-dimensional geography? It is this author's opinion that the answer to both of these questions (which are merely twentieth century versions of much older questions about determinism and free will) is *yes*, and that the resolution of the apparent paradoxes lies in the fantastic complexity and high degree of organization of the human being, complexity and organization so extraordinarily far beyond any power of prediction from the basic laws of the submicroscopic world as to constitute an independent spirit.

The basic time symmetry in the elementary-particle world has found expression recently in the "*TCP* theorem," whose three letters stand for three hypothetical operations: T, time reversal; P, space reversal which is approximately equivalent to taking a mirror image of space (this is sometimes called the parity operation, hence the P); C, charge conjugation, the technical name for interchanging particles and antiparticles. The *TCP* theorem is actually a conservation law of a special kind, and very likely an absolute conservation law governing all the interactions in nature. It says that if the three operations of T, C, and P are all applied to any physical process, the result of this mangling of what actually happened is another physical process which could have happened. This is not as complicated as it sounds; the reader may easily perform the TCP operations on any of the Feynman diagrams illustrated in these pages. All the equipment needed is one wall mirror and a little imagination.

First, turn to any page containing a "proper" Feynman diagram —one with its antiparticle arrowheads pointing downward. Figure 7.7 or any later one will do. Now, to perform the operation C, simply imagine all arrowheads turned around; this interchanges all particles and antiparticles. (A backward-pointing arrow on a photon is all right, for a photon is its own antiparticle, a property it shares with the neutral pion.) For example, the operation C converts the negative pion decay,

$$\pi^- \rightarrow \mu^- + \overline{\nu_\mu}$$

into the positive pion decay,

$$\pi^+ \rightarrow \mu^+ + \nu_\mu,$$

since the positive pion is the antiparticle of the negative pion.

To perform the operation P, space reversal, turn the page of the book away from you and look at the diagram reflected in the mirror. This interchanges left and right. (There are fuller implications of P than this, concerned with particle spin; they will be considered in Chapter Eight.)

Finally, turn the book upside down and look at the inverted diagram. This has obviously turned time around—the operation T —but it has also turned all the arrowheads around (operation C) and has interchanged left and right (operation P). The upside-down diagram therefore represents the application of all three transformations, T, C, and P, to the original physical process. The upside-down picture is another Feynman diagram that illustrates an actual, physically allowed process. In general it will not be the process you started with; it may even be quite different. But, according to the TCP theorem, since the original diagram represented a real physical process, the triply inverted diagram also does.

To see the effect of time reversal alone, we must undo the arrowhead reversal and the left-right inversion. Turn the book upside down, then look at the upside-down diagram in the mirror *and* imagine the arrowheads reversed. The diagram resulting from this manipulation illustrates the purely time-reversed process. Other combinations may be tried. The mirror view with arrowheads reversed is the result of the double operation *PC*, and so on.

The fact that the *TCP* theorem is a conservation law is not obvious, for one wonders just what quantity remains constant. Although we can define the "*TCP* quantity," study of it is not particularly instructive. It is more helpful to notice that the *TCP* theorem, like all conservation laws, is a law of prohibition. Only those events can occur, it says, whose *TCP* inversions are also possible real physical events. If the process represented by the triply inverted diagram were not allowed, then the original process would be also forbidden.

Feynman diagrams are quite useful for seeing the implications of many of the other conservation laws in a clear pictorial way. Consider, for example, the basic electron-photon vertices in Figures 7.6 and 7.7. These diagrams of fundamental annihilation and creation events illustrate several conservation laws. In each event, charge is obviously conserved. The total charge in the diagrams is either plus one or minus one or zero, and in each diagram the total charge remains the same below and above the vertex (that is, before and after the interaction event). The vertices also show the conservation of electron-family number (plus 1 for an electron, minus 1 for a positron), providing a deeper understanding of the reason the antiparticle has to be assigned a negative family number. In terms of diagrams, electron-family conservation simply means that at each fundamental vertex the number of "incoming" electron lines (one in this case) is the same as the number of "outgoing" electron lines, whether or not the arrowheads are actually pointing forward in time. A slightly more complicated example, exhibiting explicitly the conservation of charge, of baryon number, and of electron-family number, is the neutron decay shown in Figure 7.10.

Most of the Feynman diagrams presented so far represent, more or less, what is actually observed. But a few, those involving transitory intermediate particles, do not. Diagram (e) of Figure 7.3, for example, shows an intermediate or "virtual" pion exchanged between two nucleons to produce the force between them. The experimenter sees only the nucleons and must infer from their behavior that in a time of about 10^{-23} sec and over a distance of about 10^{-13} cm a pion went from one to the other. The reader may discover other virtual particles in Figures 7.5 and 7.8.

As emphasized in Chapter Six, the virtual particles play a particularly important and fascinating role in what is called self-interaction. We want to re-examine this phenomenon now pictorially with the help of Feynman diagrams. A free particle's tendency to interact with itself provides the clearest picture of the new view of the

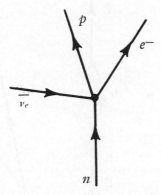

Figure 7.10. Feynman diagram for neutron decay. One baryon enters and one leaves the vertex. One member of the electron family, its neutrino, "enters" the vertex and an electron leaves. Thus two family-number conservation laws are illustrated, as is charge conservation.

submicroscopic world—a picture of continual chaotic activity, from which no particle can be isolated.

Our first guess about the world line of a single free particle (say, a proton), sitting motionless and alone in free space, might be the uninteresting vertical line of diagram (a) in Figure 7.11. As far as macroscopic observation goes, that is the whole story—an unchanging, unmoving particle tracing out its straight course through time. Since we know that nucleons and pions interact, we might inquire about the possibility of diagram (b). The proton emits a positive pion and converts itself into a neutron, the fundamental interaction event of the Yukawa theory, as illustrated, for example, by the vertices in Figure 7.3 (e). However, it is easy to see that energy conservation prohibits this process for a proton all alone. Since the proton is not moving, its total energy is just its mass energy. But neutron mass plus pion mass add up to considerably more than the proton mass. There is simply not enough energy available to create the neutron and the pion. So, as we knew already, the proton does not disintegrate into other particles.

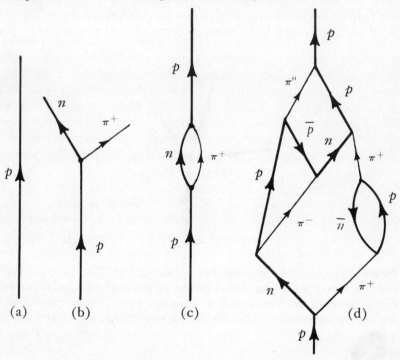

Figure 7.11. Feynman diagrams associated with a single isolated proton.

Having rejected diagram (b) and others of its type because of the prohibitions of conservation laws, we are apparently forced back to diagram (a). But as we learned from studying the consequences of the Heisenberg uncertainty principle in the last chapter, nature is willing to overlook a violation of the law of energy conservation, provided the violation lasts a short enough time. The more flagrant the violation, the briefer its duration must be. This casts a new light on diagram (b). Suppose the violation of the law of energy conservation perpetrated by the event of diagram (b) could be caused to last only a short time. It can. If the neutron reabsorbs the pion and becomes again a proton, as in diagram (c), the energy violation has been confined in time. The pion, instead of being allowed to fly off as a free particle, is never quite released. It remains a virtual particle, reabsorbed after about 10^{-23} sec, the longest time the uncertainty principle can allow this violation of energy conservation to endure.

So we must conclude that our isolated proton, if it were possible to view it through a sufficiently high-powered microscope, would be seen to be in a state of some agitation, emitting and reabsorbing pions continually, and existing part of the time as a neutron. This is the state of affairs described in Chapter Six without the help of Feynman diagrams. It leads to the picture of the proton surrounded by its swarm of virtual pions. The "high-powered microscope" needed to see this pion cloud has actually been supplied in the form of Hofstadter's high-energy electrons.

Given the possibility of transitory violation of the law of energy conservation, all sorts of complex virtual states of motion can arise. Diagram (d) in Figure 7.11—which provides the motif for this book's cover—pictures one such sequence of events, quite horrendous looking, but perfectly real. Every proton occasionally goes through exactly this dance of creation and destruction, to emerge unscathed at the other end—as well as through every other tortuous chain that is in consonance with the other conservation laws and the uncertainty principle. As far as we know, violations of charge conservation and of the three family-number conservation laws are not permitted, even for an instant of time. Therefore, at every vertex in diagram (d), these laws are satisfied. Each vertex involves an "incoming" baryon line, an "outgoing" baryon line, and a pion line. Altogether, diagram (d) includes protons, antiprotons, neutrons, antineutrons, and positive, negative, and neutral pions.

Since even a single particle alone is in such a continual state of agitation, we might ask about the still simpler situation of plain empty space. Field theory provides the answer that empty space, far from being truly void, is a rather lively place. Transitory violations of energy conservation permit particles to be formed out of nothing and vanish again. The "vacuum diagrams" illustrated in Figure 7.12 show some of the things that can (and do) transpire

in empty space. The name "physical vacuum" has been given to
space filled continually with all of these momentary comings and
goings, to distinguish it from the unreal "bare vacuum." In a similar
vein, the hypothetical, purely inert particle of diagram (a) in Figure 7.11 is termed a "bare particle" to distinguish it from the real
"physical particle" or "dressed particle" that exists part of the time
in states of activity such as were pictured in diagrams (c) and (d).

By its very complexity, diagram (d) carries a special message
about the submicroscopic world, a message of chaos: the *chaos*

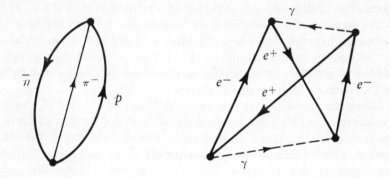

*Figure 7.12. Vacuum diagrams illustrating the transitory existence of
particles in empty space.*

provoked by the fundamental events of annihilation and creation
underlying an *order* imposed by the conservation laws. This theme
of order and chaos, already repeatedly touched upon, illustrates as
clearly as anything can the complete revolution in our view of the
world that has been brought about by the achievements of physical
science in this century.

Briefly stated, the new view is a view of chaos *beneath* order—
or, what is the same thing, of order imposed upon a deeper and
more fundamental chaos. This is in startling contrast to the view
developed and solidified in the three centuries from Kepler to
Einstein, a view of order beneath chaos. In spite of the haphazard
and unpredictable nature of the world around us, ran the old argument, nature's basic laws are fundamentally simple and orderly,

and therefore the behavior of nature at the submicroscopic level is fundamentally simple and orderly too. The building blocks of the universe are elementary objects, colorless, unemotional, identical, comprehensible and predictable, moving in calculable paths, interacting in a known way with other elementary objects.

A modern computing machine illustrates fairly well this "classical" view of elementary simplicity and orderliness. The basic elements of the machine, its transistors, are simple objects, each capable of performing only a very elementary function in a predictable and easily controllable way. The electrical engineer might be excused for waxing rhapsodic about the magnificent beauty and simplicity of the transistor and of the laws governing its action. The layman might be excused for regarding it as, on the whole, a rather dull object. But both must agree that when a few million transistors are connected together in the right way, a complicated organism comes into existence, with a rich and rewarding variety of functions and behavior patterns. A few million is a small enough number that the engineer can still undertake to predict just what the machine will do under all circumstances, but even he will be astonished by the complexity engendered by mere size.

Such was the view of the physical world until recent times. Simple objects and simple laws—a basic, underlying orderliness—lay beneath the rich chaos and complexity of the world of our senses. To lay bare the orderliness and probe to ever deeper and simpler layers of reality was the task of science, a task carried on with unprecedented speed and success in the most recent few centuries of man's existence.

But, in this century, the theories of relativity and quantum mechanics and the experimental evidence from the world of elementary particles have combined to reveal a deeper-lying and more fundamental chaos. Particles are found to have a transitory existence; empty space is a bee-hive of disordered activity; laws of probability have replaced laws of certainty; an isolated particle is engaged in a constant frenzied dance whose steps are random and unpredictable; a principle of uncertainty prevents too close scrutiny or precisely accurate measurements in the world of the very small.

This is not to say that the older idea of simplicity in the small and complexity in the large has been wholly abandoned. An electron is still a simple object, even if far from inert; nature's most fundamental laws still appear to govern the submicroscopic world;

and the complexity of size and organization is still very real. The revolution has appeared primarily in shifting the source of order from the elementary interactions and *activity* of particles to the overriding *constraints* of conservation laws. The emerging picture of the world is that of a nearly limitless chaos governed only by a set of constraining laws, a world in which apparently everything that *can* happen, subject only to the straitening effect of these conservation laws, *does* happen. The fields and particles of the submicroscopic world must be regarded as an unruly lot who carry on in every conceivable way that is not absolutely forbidden by the overriding restriction of a conservation principle.

Is this fundamental chaos of nature a temporary phenomenon in science that will be replaced by a deeper order in the future? Perhaps. There is no evidence at all upon which to base an answer to this question, but two main possibilities need to be cited. On the one hand, an elementary event of creation and annihilation which now appears to occur catastrophically at a single point in space-time may, upon closer inspection, prove to be a swift but smooth, and more orderly, unrolling of a chain of events. The probability of quantum mechanics may prove to rest only upon the great complexity of the things we now regard as simple. On the other hand, our picture of the world of the very small could easily become more chaotic, not less so. Lying dormant thus far in our picture of the world is space-time itself. While fields and particles come and go, space and time lie inert, providing the stage upon which the actors play their roles. There is some reason to believe that the future theory of particles may involve space and time as actors, not merely as stage. If so, weird convolutions of space and time and/or the quantization of space-time may contribute more to the chaos in the picture of the world.

In whatever direction the future theory of particles proceeds (and speculation on this score is rather an idle pastime, unlikely to bear fruit), it must be emphasized that present theory is much more likely to be supplemented than to be rejected. Just as Newtonian mechanics is still entirely adequate for describing the motion of planets, present theories of particles are likely to remain adequate for describing all those features of the particle world that have been understood quantitatively so far. Nevertheless, it is the deepest theory that most strongly affects our *picture* of the world, and this picture may be drastically altered in the future.

Chapter Eight

New Invariance Principles

Things and events, what is and what happens—this is the sum total of the physical world and the subject matter of science. Hand in hand with the evolution of our picture of the fundamental *things* in the world, which is now at the level of quantum fields and their manifestations as particles, has gone the development of deeper and more profound laws of the *behavior* of these things.

Yet, so far in science, our understanding of events has kept one step ahead of our understanding of things. Successful prediction of what happens at each level in the hierarchy of matter has preceded understanding of the parts of matter themselves. Consider, for example, an ordinary wristwatch. It consists of various parts—springs, balance wheel, gears, and jewels—combined into a working whole. The watchmaker understands the operation of the watch without understanding its parts. The vibration of the balance wheel and the expansion of the parts when heated can be described mathematically, and a watch of surprising accuracy can be built without any knowledge of the true nature of the parts—why a spring has elasticity, why metal expands when heated, what is the structure of a jewel. Going back not so far in history, say to 1800, there was a time when accurate watches were being built, when no one, let alone the watchmaker, had any understanding of the true nature of solid matter.

If we look deeper, say, inside one of the bits of metal within the watch, and move ahead to about 1900, we come to a time when the structure of the solid was understood as a collection of atoms. The elasticity of the solid was explained in terms of forces between the atoms; its expansion when heated was accounted for by the increased vibrational motion of the atoms. The *phenomena* of the solid were understood, but its constituent *parts*, the atoms, were not. They remained tiny building blocks whose structure and reason for being remained to be discovered.

Finally, when the behavior of the atom was unraveled after another quarter of a century, we were left again with unexplained
parts, the protons, neutrons and electrons. Today physicists are in
the position of having scored some successes (still incomplete) in
describing the behavior of elementary particles without having
any deep understanding of the field (or fields) that is the substra-
tum underlying particles. But there are some new hints that open
up one of the most challenging prospects in modern physics, hints
that perhaps we are approaching a merger of the description of
events and the description of things—that the theory of the behavior of the particles and the theory of the structure and nature of
the particles may prove to be one and the same thing.

What success has been achieved in understanding the events of
the elementary-particle world has come about in large part through
conservation laws. For a variety of reasons, as already emphasized,
these laws of constancy during change have moved to the center
of the stage in the drama of the submicroscopic world. Because
they focus on the constants of nature instead of the variables of
nature, conservation laws seem simpler than most other laws. Because of their relation to very general, and in some cases "self-
evident" principles of invariance, they seem more profound than
other laws of nature. For both reasons conservation laws have a
unique esthetic appeal. On the practical side, as more and more
conservation laws have been discovered, the idea has gained ground
that conservation laws alone may form a complete set of laws from
which all else follows. For these reasons, we end this book with a
discussion of some of the new and rather unexpected conservation
laws that govern the particle world; most of these have been
touched upon briefly in earlier chapters. The four new invariance
principles to be explained here, together with the seven absolute
conservation laws considered in Chapter Four and the conservation
of strangeness discussed in Chapter Six, constitute a nearly complete
catalogue of the important known laws constraining the behavior
of the elementary particles.

It is possible, but not yet certain, that conservation laws provide
a complete basis for the description of the *events* of the elementary-
particle world. Even much less certain, but quite possible, is the
attractive idea that exactly the same conservation laws provide the
basis for understanding the *things* of the elementary-particle world,
that is, the particles themselves. Perhaps, at last, man is probing to

that level of understanding where there is no clear distinction between what is and what happens, where the components of the world and the interaction of those components, one with another, are indistinguishable ideas.

What are the preliminary clues that point to this merging of things and events? We can cite, first of all, the material basis of our large-scale world. The same conservation laws that account for the decay of unstable particles account for the *nondecay* of electrons and protons. The stability of the basic material units of our world rests on the same conservation laws that explain the instability and interactions of the other particles. To be specific, consider the law of charge conservation. The stability of the electron as a lasting building block of the universe rests on this law. But the *behavior* of the electron rests in part on the same law, for the way in which electrons interact with photons is closely linked to the existence of the law of charge conservation.

Referring back to Figure 7.11, we recall that even an isolated particle must experience interactions. A particle *is* just fields in interaction. Its mass and other "intrinsic" properties are not really intrinsic at all, but arise from the interactions of this particle with all other particles, the form of those interactions, in turn, being dictated by conservation laws. Because of the phenomenon of self-interaction, the being and the happening are inseparable ideas. This is a new element in the scientist's view of the world, an element that has been present only for about the past thirty years. Its importance is likely to increase.

There are some other clues pointing to a merger of things and events, but mostly either more technical or more speculative. Among the former is a new "scattering matrix" theory which rejects fields and particles altogether as elementary entities. This theory (whose degree of success is still very uncertain) is a daring attempt to sweep away the *things* of the world altogether as basic elements. Instead, the interactions become fundamental, constrained by conservation laws and supplemented by conserved quantities such as energy and momentum. The objects of the world, in this theory, become subsidiary, consequences of the interaction. There is being *because* there is happening. A more radical departure from the classical view of a material basis for the world is hard to imagine.

Among the more speculative new ideas is what is sometimes

called the "geometrization of physics," the idea that space and time are all, that the actors, the action, and the stage of nature, all three, are manifestations of an underlying four-dimensional geometry of space-time. If either of these new approaches bears fruit —events as fundamental and things as secondary; or space-time as fundamental and both events and things as secondary—we shall be in for another profound revolution in our view of the world.

To avoid technical definitions, we have, so far, been rather casual about using interchangeably the phrases "conservation law" and "invariance principle." There is a difference, which was discussed in Chapter Four, and it may be well to reiterate it here, since what follows in this chapter are discussions of three invariance principles and one conservation law. An invariance principle is a statement that all laws of nature remain unchanged when some change of experimental conditions, real or hypothetical, is carried out. The mass of a muon is the same in Chicago as in New York because of the principle of invariance under change of location (the homogeneity of space). If in an experiment all particles and antiparticles are interchanged, the same laws are satisfied in the new antiexperiment. This is an invariance principle where the change of conditions may not be easy to realize in practice. A conservation law, on the other hand, is a statement that some physical quantity is unchanged during an actual physical process. That the total energy after a collision is the same as the total energy before the collision is a conservation law.

There are two significant differences here. For the invariance principle, it is the laws of nature that remain unchanged; for the conservation law, it is one specific physical quantity that remains unchanged. The invariance principle refers to a change of conditions, possibly one that is not even realizable in practice; the conservation law refers to an actual physical change. Notice also the difference between what is general and what is specific. The invariance principle: *All* laws remain unchanged for *one* particular change of conditions. The conservation law: *One* quantity remains unchanged for *all* possible physical processes.

The key point, one which is far from obvious, is that, for every invariance principle, there is an associated conservation law or, conversely, every conservation law is founded upon an invariance principle. This connection, which, in fact, is only strongly suspected, not rigorously proved, was illustrated in Chapter Four through the connection between the invariance under change of location and the conservation of momentum. That the connection between invariance and conservation is subtle is made clear enough by the fact that, for some of the conservation laws, the associated invariance principle is unknown. And the connection, even where known, seems miraculous. That a law as powerful and ubiquitous as the law of energy conservation can be founded simply upon the principle of invariance under time displacement (that natural laws are the same today as yesterday) shows the extreme power of an invariance principle.

Time Reversal

A popular way to amuse a movie audience is to run a segment of film backward—for example, to show a diver emerging feet first from the water, somersaulting upward into the air, and landing neatly (and bone-dry, with well-combed hair and a normal pulse rate) on the diving board. Everyone knows that the film is running backward because the sequence of events in the order shown is "impossible," whereas the same sequence in the opposite order— board to air to water—is perfectly possible and familiar. But suppose a doubter in the audience points out that someone might in fact have learned to swim backward with such speed and skill as to be able to hurl himself feet first from the water and actually land on the diving board as pictured. Rather far-fetched, he might admit, but is it really impossible? Can we know with absolute certainty that the film was run backward and not forward? This stickler for certainty could be assaulted with so many strong arguments that he would probably wilt quickly and join the majority to make it a unanimous decision that the film was certainly run backward. How, he might be asked, did this clever swimmer arrange for his tousled hair to comb itself as he left the water? How did he become instantly dry as he entered the air? Why did his pulse rate decrease as he propelled himself vigorously backwards through the water? How was he able, while still under the water, to gulp in bubbles of air which descended miraculously to his mouth? What set the board into vibration before he reached it? Why did a small scratch on his foot disappear as he scraped against a loose nail while landing on the board? The doubter would by this time surely have surrendered. No doubt about it, he would admit. The film was certainly run backward.

The principle of time-reversal invariance can be simply stated in terms of hypothetical moving pictures. If the filmed version of any physical process, or sequence of events, is shown backward, the viewer sees a picture of something that could have happened. In slightly more technical language, any sequence of events, if executed in the opposite order, is a physically possible sequence of events. This leads to the rather startling conclusion that it is, in fact, impossible to tell by watching a moving picture of events in nature whether the film is running backward or forward. How can this principle be reconciled with the gross violations of common sense contained in the backward view of the diver, or of a thousand other examples (think of time-reversed views of a barber cutting hair, of a rocket being launched, or a secretary typing a letter)? Does it mean that time-reversal invariance is not a valid law in the macroscopic world? No. As far as we know, time-reversal invariance is an absolute invariance, with the same universal validity as the absolute conservation laws discussed in Chapter Four. It governs every interaction in the submicroscopic world and, therefore, presumably all events in the large-scale world. The key to resolving the paradox is to recognize that possibility does not mean probability. Although the spontaneous reassembly of the fragments of an exploded bomb into a whole, unexploded bomb is wildly, ridiculously improbable, it is not impossible. It does not violate any laws of nature.

In discussing the principle of time-reversal invariance in the ordinary world around us, we are treading close to a question of some importance but one which lies outside the scope of this discussion: When does the improbable become so extremely improbable that it deserves to be called impossible? Suffice it to say that this limit is actually reached for the time-inverted views of everything that happens in the highly complex macroscopic world around us. We could wait a billion times the known lifetime of the universe and still never expect to see the time-reversed view of something even as simple as a piece of paper being torn in half. Nevertheless, it is important to realize that the time-reversed process is possible in principle.

To see that time-reversal invariance is more than a game of improbability, we must examine processes far simpler than any that have been mentioned so far. Suppose a space traveler bound for another galaxy takes along a moving picture of our solar system to show his hosts. If the picture had been taken from a point a few hundred billion miles distant in the general direction of the north star, it would show the planets as tiny dots tracing out their elliptical orbits in a counter-clockwise direction about a central sun. The creatures of the other galaxy, being well versed in the laws of mechanics, would watch the picture with interest and conclude that there were no tricks, that it did indeed depict an actual physical chain of events. But had the film been run off backward, they would have been equally convinced. The backward view of planetary motion, although "untrue," since, in fact, our planets do not move that way, is nevertheless "possible," for it is consistent with the same laws of mechanics.

Now allow our space traveler to proceed on to another galaxy whose residents are intelligent and mathematically adept, but scientifically primitive. One audience of these creatures is shown the planetary film in the forward direction; another audience is shown the same film run backward. Both audiences are asked to deduce the law of gravitational attraction and the law of mechanical motion from what they have seen. If they are collectively as clever as Newton, they will put their heads together and both groups will arrive at the correct, and identical, laws.

This is the real significance of time-reversal invariance. Under a hypothetical reversal of the direction of time, all of the laws of nature are unchanged. This is the statement of the principle that emphasizes *invariance*. To emphasize the *constraint* imposed by the law, we must phrase it somewhat differently. Only those things can happen that could also happen in the opposite order. Or, still more negatively: if a time-reversed process is impossible, then the process itself must be impossible.

Time-reversal invariance finds its simplest application in the world of particles, where it appears to govern every interaction, strong, weak, and electromagnetic. Figure 8.1, for example, illustrates electron-positron annihilation. The time-reversed process, also possible, is the creation of an electron-positron pair by the collision of two photons. Recall the directions given in Chapter Seven for time-inverting a Feynman diagram. Turn the page upside down, view it in a wall mirror, and mentally turn the arrows around. You then see two photons coming together from the bottom, and an electron and a positron flying apart at the top. According to time-reversal invariance, this reverse process is not only possible, but can occur in every detail as the inverted sequence of fundamental interaction events. Since the "strength" of interaction at each vertex is unchanged, there is a definite numerical ratio between the probability of pair creation and the probability of pair annihilation which is implied by the law.

The role of probability in time-reversed events, so painfully obvious for the diver shooting backward out of the water, makes itself felt in the particle world as well. A simple process of pion

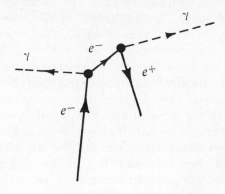

Figure 8.1. Feynman diagram for electron-positron annihilation.

creation, for example, is impossible to reverse in practice. Two protons may collide to yield proton, neutron, and positive pion, as shown in Figure 8.2. The time-reversed process requires the nearly simultaneous collision of three particles, too unlikely to achieve in practice. But the requirement that *each* fundamental event is time reversible is a constraining condition that influences the possible form of the pion-nucleon interaction and therefore has an important effect on the forward-in-time process, whether or not the time-reversed process is likely, or experimentally possible. This is an exceedingly important aspect of invariance principles related to their increasingly central role in physics. The laws of mechanics to which our diver is subjected are partially determined by the condition of time-reversal invariance. Therefore, the particular way in which the diver arcs through the air is dictated in part by time-reversal invariance, even though it is entirely out of the question for him to execute the maneuver in reverse.

Everything in the everyday world of our sense experience makes plain that there is a unique direction of time, an irrevocable forward flow. Studies of elementary-particle interactions, on the other hand, reveal that one direction of time is just as good as another. The laws of nature are completely symmetric between forward and backward in time. This puzzle finds its resolution in the idea of probability. Given any sequence of events, one order of execut-

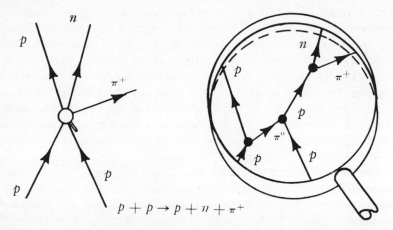

$$p + p \rightarrow p + n + \pi^+$$

Figure 8.2. Creation of a pion in a proton-proton collision. The time-reversed process is possible but far less likely than the direct process.

ing them will be more likely than the opposite order. For very simple events, in the particle world, a given process and the time-reversed process may be almost equally likely. But the more complicated and elaborate the sequence of events, the more overwhelming is the probability of one order relative to the opposite order. Since everything of which man is directly aware is, on the scale of elementary particles, extremely complex, we know only the unfolding of events in the direction of high probability, a direction we define as the "true" direction of time. It is a stimulating idea that the only reason man is aware of the past and not the future is that he is a complicated and highly organized structure. Unfortunately, simpler creatures are no better off. They equalize future and past by remembering neither. An electron, being precisely identical with every other electron, is totally unmarked by its past or by its future. Man is intelligent enough to be scarred by his past. But the same complexity that gives him a memory at all is what keeps his future a mystery.

Parity

The parity principle, or the principle of space-inversion invariance, says that there is a symmetry between the world and its mirror image. To state this in terms closer to what we used for time-reversal invariance: The mirror image of any physical process depicts a possible physical process, one that is governed by the same laws as the process itself. Most of us perform parity transformations every day, whenever we look in a mirror. Now there is nothing "strange" about a mirror view of most things or most events. A mirror view is not "right," but it appears quite reasonable and possible. The mirror view of a person may not be an exact replica of any person, but we are quite prepared to believe that a real person *could* appear just that way.

The mirror view of a printed page looks "wrong." It is obviously quite different from the direct view of the page. But there is nothing impossible about it. A printer could design inverted type and produce a page which, viewed directly, would be identical with the mirror view of the normal page. Most children put this symmetry to work by learning "mirror writing," which appears normal only when viewed in a mirror (see Figure 8.3).

The situation with the space-inverted view of the normal world differs completely from that with the time-inverted view. The mirror view of the world looks quite normal, on the whole, and prepares us to believe in parity conservation, or space-inversion invariance. The time-reversed view of the world, on the other hand, looks ridiculous and impossible and prepares us to resist the idea of time-reversal invariance. The particles have fooled us on both counts. Time-reversal invariance proves to be an absolute conservation law, so far as we know now, and space-inversion invariance turns out to be only a partial conservation law, one that is violated by the weak interactions. This means that the mirror view of an actual weak interaction process such as beta decay shows something that *can not* happen. Even scientists had discarded their normal caution, and come to regard parity conservation as an absolute law. When, following a suggestion by Tsung Dao Lee and Chen Ning Yang, it was verified in 1956 that the weak interactions

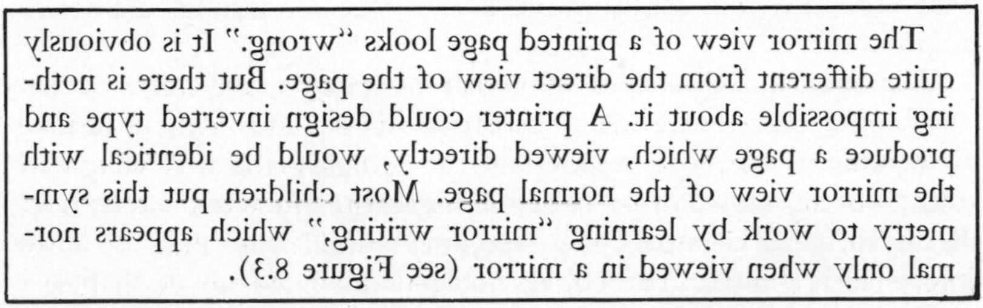

The mirror view of a printed page looks "wrong." It is obviously quite different from the direct view of the page. But there is nothing impossible about it. A printer could design inverted type and produce a page which, viewed directly, would be identical with the mirror view of the normal page. Most children put this symmetry to work by learning "mirror writing," which appears normal only when viewed in a mirror (see Figure 8.3).

Figure 8.3. Parity transformation applied to a printed page.

do *not* have mirror symmetry,* it came as rather a shock to the scientific community, a useful reminder that an untested theory is a house built on sand.

A slide projector or a movie projector is a better device than a mirror for illustrating the idea of parity conservation in the everyday world. Most of us are so accustomed to mirrors that we mentally compensate for the space-inversion in the mirror view. But, with a projector, an element of mystery can be introduced that makes the invariance more obvious. If you were shown an unfamiliar landscape on the screen, you would be quite unable to tell whether the slide had been inserted correctly or the wrong way around. It would look reasonable and possible in either case. Even for a moving picture with the film inverted left for right, it might be difficult to decide whether you were seeing the true view or the space-inverted view. Of course, if nine out of ten of the actors seemed to be left-handed, or if cars in an American city were being driven on the left, or if a sign-post showed backward writing, the secret would be out. But, even with these clues to give the show away, nothing in the inverted view would violate common sense or be obviously impossible. This is no mere coincidence. The fact that mirror views of the ordinary world look perfectly reasonable is directly connected with the fact that all of the laws of

---

* For this prediction and related work, Lee and Yang shared the Nobel prize in physics in 1957. At the time they challenged the law of parity conservation, Lee was 29 years old and Yang was 33.

nature which govern the large-scale world obey the principle of space-inversion invariance. If they did not—if, for example, the weak interactions had any direct effect on the world of our sense experiences—we should be made obviously aware that a mirror view of an actual sequence of events was all wrong, a physical impossibility.

The radioactive nucleus of cobalt 60 (Co^{60}), the same nucleus that could represent a major threat to human life in the aftermath of a nuclear war, was responsible for bringing the first enlightenment on the violation of parity conservation in weak interactions. Reduced to its essentials, the experiment of Chien-Shiung Wu was exceedingly simple. The cobalt nuclei were lined up so that their intrinsic rotational motion, viewed from the top, was counterclockwise. See the "direct view" in the upper left of Figure 8.4, which shows a Co^{60} nucleus with its "north pole" on top, its "south pole" on the bottom. In the experiment, a large number of Co^{60} nuclei were oriented in exactly the same way. It was then observed that, as the nuclei, one by one, underwent their explosive process of beta decay, the ejected electrons almost all flew off in the downward direction. The solid arrows in the diagram represent the preferred flight direction of the electrons. Now, the mirror view of this process shows a Co^{60} nucleus apparently rotating in the opposite direction, but with the electrons still coming out mostly downward. (It is to be borne in mind, of course, that a single Co^{60} nucleus only ejects one electron.) If, on the other hand, the whole experimental apparatus, including all the nuclei, were turned upside down, the direction of rotation of the nuclei would be changed *and* and the direction of emission of the electrons would also be changed. The inescapable conclusion is that the upside-down view and the mirror view of the original process are inconsistent with each other. One or the other of them (or both!) must be impossible.

Our first inclination is to say that the upside-down view is obviously possible. There is nothing to prevent the experimenter from turning his apparatus upside down or, more simply, from turning himself upside down, to get a new view of the process. This is quite correct, although it is important to realize that this obviousness rests upon an invariance principle, the isotropy of space, which underlies the law of angular-momentum conservation. That an upside-down experiment must yield the same results as the original experiment is "obvious" only to the extent that our everyday experience conditions us to accept the invariance of laws of nature under rotations as a self-evident truth. In fact, we have strong reasons to believe in angular-momentum conservation and the uniformity of space as absolute laws. Therefore the upside-down

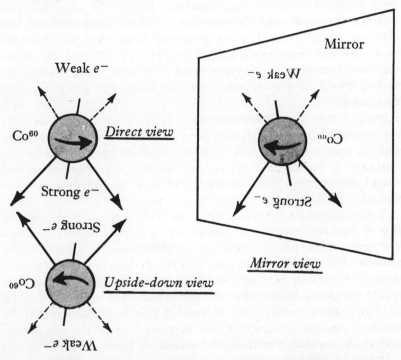

Figure 8.4. Decay of an oriented Co⁶⁰ nucleus and other views of the process. The turned-around labels are without significance. Only the physically measurable things have meaning in the various views.

view of the Co⁶⁰ beta-decay process is indeed a picture of a physically possible process.

To someone who believed with equal conviction in the invariance of laws of nature under space inversion, it would be equally "obvious" that the mirror view must also represent a physically possible process. Most physicists were nearly in that position. All of the classical laws of physics possessed mirror invariance, and in the quantum world of particles it was already known that the strong interactions and the electromagnetic interactions possessed mirror invariance. Parity conservation was in danger of becoming a self-evident truth. Yet the mirror view of the Co^{60} experiment certainly represented an impossible process. Mirror invariance for the weak interactions had to be abandoned. It must be admitted that, even for physicists, the common sense derived from everyday experience is still a much more powerful force than the common sense derived from mathematical insight. The failure of space-rotation invariance would have caused an even more violent stir in the world of science than did the failure of space-inversion invariance.

Imagine that there exist some tiny creatures whose everyday life is strongly affected by the weak interactions. They would probably find the mirror view of the Co^{60} decay quite diverting. They would recognize at once that it showed an absurdly impossible event and would perhaps find it as amusing as we find the picture of a diver shooting feet first from the water.

The value of every conservation law or invariance principle is that it imposes constraints, restricting nature's freedom. For the Co^{60} experiment, mirror invariance would require that just as many electrons fly up as down, in fact, that the pattern of emerging electrons is exactly symmetric between up and down, for only then would the upside-down view and the mirror view agree. If the law of parity conservation were suspended this restriction would be removed and the electrons would be permitted to fly out in any way at all (consistent with *other* conservation laws).

Why did more than fifty years elapse between the discovery of beta decay and the discovery that the beta-decay process lacks mirror invariance? There is a simple technical reason for this. The Co^{60} experiment was actually a good deal more complicated than our discussion has indicated. Lining up nuclei all to rotate in the same direction is a difficult process, for it is hard to get a "handle" on them. And once lined up, they tend to flop about and soon get entirely disoriented again. The constant thermal agitation in every material fights against efforts to arrange the nuclei in an orderly fashion. It is clear that the Co^{60} experiment would have been useless had half of the nuclei been spinning one way and half the other way. In that case, as many electrons would have come out upward as downward and nothing would have been learned about mirror invariance. To line up the nuclei and keep them that way, Mrs.

Wu enlisted the aid of a group at the National Bureau of Standards who were expert at achieving very low temperatures. At a temperature of less than one tenth of a degree above absolute zero, the thermal agitation was reduced sufficiently that the cobalt nuclei could be maintained with oriented spins, and the desired experiment could be carried out.*

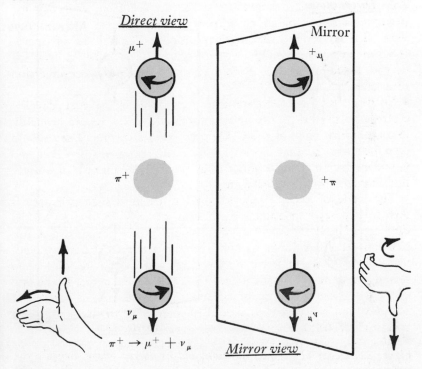

Figure 8.5. The left-handed neutrino created in the decay of a positive pion, and its right-handed mirror image.

Among the many further proofs of the failure of mirror invariance, none is simpler or more convincing than the discovery that the neutrino is left-handed. The mirror view of a left-handed neutrino (Figure 8.5) is a right-handed neutrino, but there is no

---

* Actually, temperatures less than one degree cannot be maintained for very long. The cobalt was cooled to about one one-hundredth of a degree and the measurement carried out during the ten minutes required for the well-insulated material to warm up to one degree.

such thing as a right-handed neutrino; therefore the mirror view is a view of the impossible.

So far we have emphasized the *failure* of parity conservation, but in all but the weak interactions it is a powerful and valid law limiting what can happen. For example, had the Co^{60} nuclei undergone

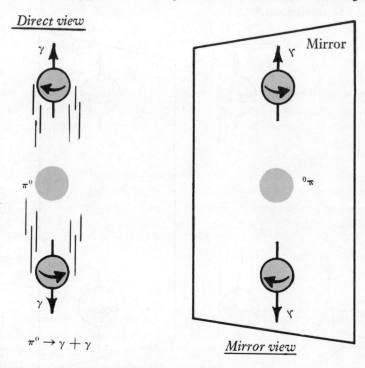

Figure 8.6. Decay of the neutral pion, and its mirror image. Because the interactions governing this decay possess mirror invariance, the mirror view pictures a possible mode of neutral pion decay. The photons may be either left-handed or right-handed.

gamma decay instead of beta decay, as many photons would have emerged upward as downward. In that case, only the electromagnetic interaction would have been at work, not the weak interaction, and mirror invariance would have required the symmetric result.

Similarly, the decay of the neutral pion into two photons,

$$\pi^0 \rightarrow \gamma + \gamma,$$

which is the result of the combined action of strong and electromagnetic interactions, is quite different from the weak decay of the charged pion. Suppose, for a particular decay, that the photons come out left-handed, as did the muon and neutrino in Figure 8.5. The mirror view of this process (Figure 8.6) shows right-handed photons, so mirror invariance requires that decay into right-handed photons is also possible. In fact, it requires that decay into right-handed photons is exactly equally probable, for all the laws of nature (governing *this* process) are the same in the mirror world as in the real world. If decay into left-handed photons were preferred, by however small a margin, in the real world, then right-handed photons would be preferred by the same margin in the mirror world, and this would be a violation of space-inversion invariance.

In prequantum physics, parity conservation was recognized but thought to be unimportant. In quantum physics its power was recognized because of restrictions it imposed on the flow of events governed by laws of probability. Now it has become doubly important through the discovery that some interactions obey the law and some do not. A good reason why the weak interactions are parity violators has yet to be found.

Charge Conjugation

The third member of the *T, P, C* triumvirate is charge conjugation, the interchange of particles and antiparticles. As emphasized in the last chapter, the fact that particle-antiparticle inversion has anything to do with time inversion and space inversion comes about because antiparticles may be described as particles moving backward in time. Hand in hand with the overthrow of parity went the less heralded overthrow of charge-conjugation invariance. The present situation is this. *T* invariance seems to be an absolute law. The combination of *P* invariance plus *C* invariance is also an absolute law, and therefore the *TCP* theorem, which says that all three inversions taken together form an absolute invariance principle, is true. For the strong interactions and the electromagnetic interactions *C* invariance and P invariance are separately valid laws. The weak interactions violate both *C* invariance and *P* invariance, but are restricted by combined *CP* invariance.

The left-handed neutrino, which violates space-inversion invariance, also violates charge-conjugation invariance. Consider, for example, the decay of the positive pion, written symbolically:

$$\pi^+ \rightarrow \mu_L^+ + \nu_{\mu L}.$$

The subscripts L indicate that neutrino and positive muon fly apart with left-handed spin. We know that the action of C on this process is to interchange particles and antiparticles, while the action of P is to convert left-handed motion to right-handed motion. Thus we get the following transformed processes:

$$C: \quad \pi^- \rightarrow \mu_L^- + \overline{\nu_{\mu L}}, \qquad \text{No.}$$
$$P: \quad \pi^+ \rightarrow \mu_R^+ + \nu_{\mu R}, \qquad \text{No.}$$
$$PC: \quad \pi^- \rightarrow \mu_R^- + \overline{\nu_{\mu R}}, \qquad \text{Yes.}$$

The C transformation leads to an "impossible" process (one that has never been seen), since it converts a left-handed neutrino to a left-handed antineutrino, but antineutrinos are right-handed. Therefore this weak interaction decay violates C invariance. The P transformation converts the left-handed neutrino into a right-handed neutrino, giving again a process that has never been seen. But P and C together change the left-handed neutrino to a right-handed antineutrino. The last line in our list of symbolic decays represents what is actually seen in the decay of the negative pion. The PC transformation applied to a physically allowed process yields a process that is also physically allowed. Through this and a number of other examples, it has been verified that even the undisciplined weak interactions do not violate the combined PC invariance.

To complete the TCP picture, we list the results of two more kinds of inversion on the process of positive pion decay:

$$T: \quad \nu_{\mu L} + \mu_L^+ \rightarrow \pi^+, \qquad \text{Yes.}$$
$$TCP: \quad \overline{\nu_{\mu R}} + \mu_R^- \rightarrow \pi^-, \qquad \text{Yes.}$$

Time inversion alone changes the order of events in the original process. All three inversions together change left to right, particles to antiparticles, and before to after. Each of these transformed processes is almost certainly physically possible, but there is no hope of testing either of them experimentally.

Although the left-handed neutrino is a parity violator and a charge-conjugation violator, it is probably not the answer to the question: *Why* do the weak interactions violate P invariance and

C invariance? Some processes that do not involve neutrinos nevertheless violate these conservation laws. It is known, for example, that, in the decay of the lambda particle,

$$\Lambda^0 \rightarrow p + \pi^-,$$

the proton tends to come off in the direction in which the "north pole" of the lambda was pointing, and the pion in the opposite, or

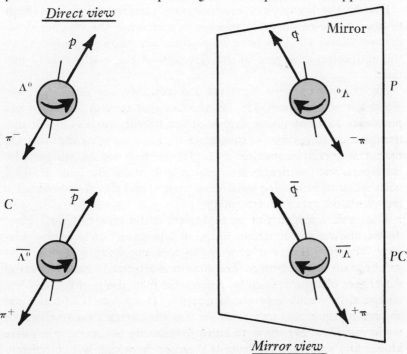

Figure 8.7. *Decay of an oriented lambda particle into proton and negative pion, with other views of the same process.*

"south pole" direction. This process is indicated in the upper left-hand diagram of Figure 8.7. (Recall that if the fingers of the right hand are curved around in the direction of spin rotation, the right thumb points to the north pole.) This asymmetry of decay violates *P* invariance, for, in the mirror image, the proton is seen to emerge in the south-pole direction, contrary to what would happen if the Λ^0 particle had simply been turned upside down.

The lower left-hand diagram pictures the hypothetical process resulting from particle-antiparticle exchange:

$$\overline{\Lambda^0} \to \overline{p} + \pi^+.$$

Although the preferred direction of emission of the pion has not yet been observed in the decay of the antilambda, other less direct evidence makes it certain that the pictured process will *not* happen.

Finally, the lower right-hand diagram pictures the mirror image of the charge-conjugation process, representing the combined action of P and C. This is again a physically allowed process, with the antiproton emerging in the direction of the antilambda's south pole.

No one knows why the weak interactions obey only the combined law of PC invariance, but the fact that they do so has caused physicists to think more deeply about mirror images. Essentially, the question raised by PC invariance is: How do we *know* that the mirror image of a particle is a particle and not an antiparticle? Perhaps particle-antiparticle inversion goes naturally hand in hand with space inversion for some deep reason, and the PC combination represents the "true" mirror image.

The same question can be rephrased at the classical level: How do we know that the mirror image of a positive charge is also positive? The only way we know the sign of any electric charge is by its effect on other charges. The proton is arbitrarily called positive. Any other charge repelled by a proton is then also positive, and any charge attracted by a proton is negative. If we watch a proton and an electron in a mirror we can see that they attract each other, but we have no way whatever to know that we are not seeing a negative proton and a positive electron. It is rather surprising but completely self-consistent to suppose that the mirror performs for us the action of charge conjugation as well as space inversion. In that case, what we see in a mirror always represents a physically allowed process, for the weak interactions as well as the strong. This sounds as though we have magically caused the mirror to change what it shows us by speaking the right words over it. Of course, what we see in the mirror has not changed. The point is that, in part, we did not know *what* we were seeing. It was a mere assumption that the image of a proton was a proton. If we choose to make the opposite assumption (which careful reasoning will show no one can disprove) that the image of the proton is an antiproton, then

PC invariance appears to be more "natural." The next time you look in a mirror, reflect that you may be seeing an antiman.

Isotopic Spin

Every fact of nature finds its origin in a conservation law. This appealing, but still unproved, assertion receives some support from the history of our final two conservation laws—strangeness and isotopic spin.

The strange facts of the rapid production and slow decay of the new particles, the existence of some processes and the absence of others, found a simple explanation in terms of the conservation of some new property of matter which was christened strangeness. Its underlying invariance principle remains unknown. All we know is that if, to every particle, we assign a strangeness number—in addition to its charge and spin and baryon- or electron- or muon-family number—then the conservation of strangeness in strong interactions serves to account for a large array of experimental facts, in particular, for the absence of a number of processes that should otherwise be observed.

Isotopic spin, with an even more peculiar name than strangeness, is a property of the same type. It is some extra "thing" carried by the strongly interacting particles, and the total amount of this "thing" remains unchanged during all strong interaction processes. Unfortunately, isotopic spin is not just a number that can be assigned to each particle. It behaves like a vector, a quantity with both magnitude and direction. To make matters worse, the isotopic-spin vector does not point in any direction in ordinary space, but exists in an entirely different space, outside the range of man's perception, something called isotopic-spin space, or simply *I* space.

It should be obvious that not even the boldest and most imaginative physicist would have dared to suggest seriously concepts like this unless driven to do so by the accumulated weight of experimental evidence. At every step along the road from the common-sense picture of the large-scale world around us to the remarkably different and very non-common-sense view of the world of the very small, man has embraced strange new concepts only when they afforded the simplest possible explanation of some collection of experimental facts. Sometimes, new experimental facts suggested directly a new picture, as when the photoelectric effect suggested the photon. Sometimes the new picture evolved slowly, and with the help of mathematics. Heisenberg's theory of quantum mechanics, for example, was a complete success as a mathematical description of atomic phenomena well before its full conceptual content was realized. The revolutionary picture of the world implied by quantum mechanics was developed over a period of years as more and more of the mathematical consequences of the theory were worked out.

In order to see how the concept of the invisible and not directly knowable *I* space made its way into physics, we must move back to 1932 and the discovery of the neutron. The previously known particles, the electron, the photon and the proton, were very different from one another. But the new particle, the neutron, very obviously belonged with the proton. Neutron and proton had nearly the same mass, they were both constituents of nuclei, and they attracted each other with a powerful new force. Werner Heisenberg, immediately impressed by this relationship, seized on the similarities, and, in the same year, showed that neutron and proton could be regarded as two states of a *single* particle, the nucleon. His mathematical trick, described in words, will hardly seem worth the effort. It required the invention of the new *I* space, in which the nucleon is a vector which may point "up" (nothing to do with the "up" of ordinary space) or "down." If it points up, we see it as a proton. If it points down, we see it as a neutron. If two or more nucleons exist together, as in a nucleus, their separate *I* vectors may add up to a total *I* vector which may point up, down, or in other possible directions.

According to the Heisenberg picture, the nucleon is a "doublet," that is, it can exist in just two possible states, as neutron or as proton. But this was not the first such doublet behavior noticed in nature. A particle with one half unit of spin, such as the proton or the electron, could exist with its spin pointing either up or down (in *ordinary* space). This is because the quantum theory requires that adjacent values of angular momentum (or spin) must differ by one whole unit. If an electron spin of one half unit points upward, the only way it can change by one whole unit is to turn over and point downward—from plus $\frac{1}{2}$ to minus $\frac{1}{2}$. On the other hand, if a particle had one unit of spin, it could point in three different directions, up, down, and halfway between—plus 1, minus 1, and zero. Now, Heisenberg's trick of describing proton and neutron as two states of the same particle was mathematically equivalent to the description of spin, so the new property of the nucleon, the direction it points in the hypothetical *I* space, was also named a kind of spin, a poor name, in fact, since it has nothing whatever to do with ordinary spin. Since the change of a neutron to a proton changes one nucleus to another, and since individual nuclei are sometimes called isotopes,* the new kind of "spin" was labeled isotopic spin. For a group of nucleons, a rotation of the total isotopic-spin vector in *I* space corresponds to changing from one nucleus to another without changing the total number of nucleons.

Some years had to elapse before it could be decided whether Heisenberg's *I* space was mere mathematical construction or something with real physical content. The decision in favor of its real significance rested on two developments. First of all, as new particles were discovered, they were found to come in closely linked groups, like proton and neutron. There were three pions which formed a triplet and could be described as three states of a single pion with one unit of isotopic spin. The sigma particles also formed a triplet, and the kaons, like the nucleons, a doublet. Thus the kaon was assigned one-half unit of isotopic spin. The lambda particle stands alone as a singlet; it has zero isotopic spin.

Second, and more important, an isotopic-spin conservation law is found to be obeyed by the strong interactions. Technically this means that the probability of any process, or the strength of any interaction, is unchanged if the total isotopic-spin vector is rotated in *I* space. One consequence of this law, for example, is that the interaction between a proton and a positive pion must be exactly the same as that between a neutron and a negative pion, for the change from $(p + \pi^+)$ to $(n + \pi^-)$ is equivalent to turning over both the nucleon and pion isotopic spins, from "up" to "down."

There are a wealth of consequences of isotopic spin conservation, but most of them are difficult to picture. Roughly, however, the significance of the law can be understood simply as independence of charge. In the strong interactions, nature does not care how much electric charge a particle carries. Proton and neutron are on

---

* All nuclei with the same number of protons belong to a given *element*. Each *isotope* of that element contains a different number of neutrons. Thus, all cobalt nuclei contain 27 protons. Cobalt 60 is the particular isotope of cobalt with 27 protons and 33 neutrons.

an equal footing; positive, negative and neutral pion all interact in the same way. It is as if different charges come in different colors and the strong interactions can see only black and white.

A photon, on the other hand, can see the colors very clearly. It interacts with charged particles, but not with neutral particles. Therefore the electromagnetic interactions violate the law of isotopic-spin conservation. As far as we know now, this is the *only* conservation law not common to the strong interactions and the electromagnetic interactions. The reason? No one knows.

It should not be surprising to learn that the weak interactions also flaunt the law of isotopic-spin conservation. In the decay of the lambda, for example,

$$\Lambda^0 \to p + \pi^- \qquad \text{or} \qquad \Lambda^0 \to n + \pi^0,$$

the initial isotopic spin is zero. But the final nucleon has one-half unit of isotopic spin and the final pion one unit. These two can combine to a total of either one half or three halves, in either case different from zero. According to present evidence, the lambda chooses the less flagrant violation, going to the final combination with one-half unit.

The strong interactions are hemmed in by twelve conservation laws:

Energy
Momentum
Angular momentum
Charge
Electron-family number
Muon-family number
Baryon number
Time reversal (T)
Combined space inversion and charge conjugation (PC)
Space inversion alone (P) [and charge conjugation alone (C)]
Strangeness
Isotopic spin

Unfortunately, these do not yet quite realize the goal of determining uniquely the form of the strong interactions from conservation laws alone, but they provide very powerful inhibitions on what can happen in nature. It is not far from the truth to say that the whole structure of the world as we know it is determined by the fact that in all processes of change—in all the *activity* in the world—some or all of these quantities remain constant.

Going down the ladder of strengths, isotopic-spin conservation is lost at the next lower rung, the electromagnetic interactions. Stepping down to the weak interactions, strangeness conservation, parity conservation, and charge-conjugation invariance are lost, but the combination *PC* remains valid. The last downward step, to the gravitational interactions at the submicroscope level, has not yet been taken. Whether more conservation laws will fall by the way-side at this last step is a fascinating open question for the future.

Elementary particles have been the natural proving ground for the two great theories of this century, relativity and quantum mechanics; for the fundamental idea that fields are the primordial stuff of the universe; and for the hypothesis that invariance principles and conservation laws are the heart and soul of the laws of nature from which all else flows.

In the seventeenth century, man looked upward and outward into the universe and was humbled, as his earth took its diminutive place as a speck of matter in a corner of the cosmos. In this century, we look downward and inward and find new reasons for humility. Where we might have expected to find some firm lumps of matter as the building blocks of man and his world, we find a chaos of annihilation and creation, a swarm of transitory bits of matter, and the tenuous substance of wave fields. Where we might have expected to find laws of certainty, we find laws of probability, and seem to see the hand of chance working at every turn—chance that any particles are stable, chance that the neutron can live forever within a nucleus, chance that we are free of the threat of annihilation by antiparticles. Above the chaos and the probability stand the conservation laws, imposing their order upon the undisciplined energy of the universe to make possible the marvellously intricate, incredibly organized structures of the stable world of our senses.

Progress in science requires the ability to know how to ask the right questions. The present era in physics is a particularly challenging one, and likely to be a fruitful one because we know enough to ask a great many questions, at least some of which will undoubtedly prove to be important. Why does mass come only in lumps of certain size? Why is baryon number conserved? Are fields real? Are space and time actors or only a stage of action? And many more which have been posed in these pages. The faith in simplicity, which has been the most powerful single stimulus to scientific inquiry throughout history, still provides the primary motivation for attacking these questions. Most scientists share a firm faith that these questions have simple answers and that there are deeper and more fundamental layers of matter and energy and space and time still to be uncovered.

Bibliography

Unstarred references are technical articles primarily for the specialist. Singly-starred references, although intended for a scientific audience, are readable by the non-specialist. Doubly-starred references are intended for the general reader.

GENERAL WORKS, MAINLY EXPOSITORY

** ALBERT EINSTEIN and LEOPOLD INFELD, *The Evolution of Physics* (New York: Simon and Shuster, 1961). A lucid account of the development of physical thinking from the mechanical view of the seventeenth century to the twentieth century view of space, time, and fields.

** BERTRAND RUSSELL, *The ABC of Relativity* (New York: New American Library, 1959). A non-mathematical and well-written presentation of the ideas of relativity and of the altered view of nature generated by relativity theory. (Russell's book is referred to on p. 102.)

** VICTOR F. WEISSKOPF, *Knowledge and Wonder* (Garden City: Doubleday and Company, Inc., 1963). A beautiful summary of some fundamentals of physics, chemistry, and biology without mathematics.

** DAVID H. FRISCH and ALAN M. THORNDIKE, *Elementary Particles* (Princeton, New Jersey: D. Van Nostrand Company, Inc., 1964). This book, intended for students and general readers of above-average technical background, includes descriptions of some important tools and experiments of elementary-particle physics.

** R. D. HILL, *Tracking Down Particles* (New York: W. A. Benjamin, Inc., 1963). A straightforward and very readable account of elementary particles.

** STAFF OF THE LAWRENCE RADIATION LABORATORY, University of California, Berkeley, *Introduction to the Detection of Nuclear Particles in a Bubble Chamber* (Cambridge, Mass.: The Ealing Press, 1964). This booklet is notable for its fourteen stereoscopic bubble chamber photographs. It comes equipped with a collapsible viewer.

GENERAL WORKS, MAINLY HISTORICAL

* SIR EDMUND WHITTAKER, *A History of the Theories of Aether and Electricity* (New York: Harper and Bros., 1960), vol. 2, *The Modern*

Theories 1900–1926. This authoritative history, a rich source of references to fundamental papers, is very uneven in its mathematical level, only parts of it being suitable for the general reader. Whittaker is somewhat overzealous to minimize the contributions of Albert Einstein to relativity theory.

** CHEN NING YANG, *Elementary Particles: A Short History of Some Discoveries in Atomic Physics* (Princeton, N. J.: Princeton University Press, 1961). Perhaps better described as exposition in historical context than as history, this well-written distillation of ideas and discoveries in modern physics reflects the insights and the style of a creative contemporary physicist.

** LAURA FERMI, *Atoms in the Family* (Chicago: University of Chicago Press, 1954). This personal view of Enrico Fermi's life and work is both informative and entertaining.

** JEREMY BERNSTEIN, "A Question of Parity," *The New Yorker*, May 12, 1962, p. 49. This profile of T. D. Lee and C. N. Yang gives an excellent view of the people and the ideas that played major roles when the non-conservation of parity in weak interactions was demonstrated.

** THE EDITORS of *Fortune, Great American Scientists* (Englewood Cliffs, N.J.: Prentice-Hall, Inc., 1960). Thirty pages of this book describe contemporary physics in America in human terms. Current problems and ideas are cleverly interwoven with brief biographical sketches.

PAPERS OF REVIEW AND EXPLANATION

** F. REINES and C. L. COWAN, JR., "Neutrino Physics," *Physics Today*, vol. 10, no. 8, p. 12 (August, 1957). A report on the neutrino detection experiment of the authors, with historical background.

** JOHN A. WHEELER and SEYMOUR TILSON, "The Dynamics of Space-Time," *International Science and Technology*, December, 1963, p. 62. The ideas of "geometrodynamics," Wheeler's theory of space-time alone as the basis of the material world, are set forth with force and clarity.

** The *Scientific American* (published monthly by Scientific American, Inc., New York) is the richest source of authoritative, well-written and well-illustrated articles on modern physics (as well as other branches of science). Among articles of interest in recent years are the following:

FREEMAN J. DYSON, "Field Theory," April, 1953.

PHILIP MORRISON, "The Neutrino," January, 1956.

HERMAN YAGODA, "The Tracks of Nuclear Particles," May, 1956.

EMILIO SEGRÈ and CLYDE WIEGAND, "The Antiproton," June, 1956.

ROBERT HOFSTADTER, "The Atomic Nucleus," July, 1956.

JOHN M. BLATT, "Time Reversal," August, 1956.

ROBERT MARSHAK, "Pions," January, 1957.

PHILIP MORRISON, "The Overthrow of Parity," April, 1957.

GEORGE GAMOW, "The Principle of Uncertainty," January, 1958.

ROBERT R. WILSON, "Particle Accelerators," March, 1958.

S. B. TREIMAN, "The Weak Interactions," March, 1959.

SHELDON PENMAN, "The Muon," July, 1961.

E. L. GINZTON and WILLIAM KIRK, "The Two-Mile Accelerator," November, 1961.

GERARD K. O'NEILL, "The Spark Chamber," August, 1962.

R. D. HILL, "Resonance Particles," January, 1963.

LEON M. LEDERMAN, "The Two-Neutrino Experiment," March, 1963.

P. A. M. DIRAC, "The Evolution of the Physicist's Picture of Nature," May, 1963.

G. FEINBERG and M. GOLDHABER, "Conservation Laws," October, 1963.

GOEFFREY F. CHEW, MURRAY GELL-MANN, and ARTHUR H. ROSENFELD, "Strongly Interacting Particles," February, 1964.

The *Annual Review of Nuclear Science* (Palo Alto, California: Annual Reviews, Inc.) is a good source of technical articles reviewing new developments in physics. Among recent articles related to elementary particles—none of them easy reading—are the following:

DONALD J. HUGHES, "Neutron Optics," vol. 3, p. 93 (1953).

*WILLIAM B. FRETTER, "Nuclear Particle Detection (Cloud Chambers and Bubble Chambers)," vol. 5, p. 145 (1955).

EMILIO SEGRÈ, "Antinucleons," vol. 8, p. 127 (1958).

DAVID L. JUDD, "Conceptual Advances in Accelerators," vol. 8, p. 181 (1958).

*FREDERICK REINES, "Neutrino Interactions," vol. 10, p. 1 (1960).

HUGH BRADNER, "Bubble Chambers," vol. 10, p. 109 (1960).

ARTHUR H. ROSENFELD and WILLIAM E. HUMPHREY, "Analysis of Bubble Chamber Data," vol. 13, p. 103 (1963).

A. H. ROSENFELD, A. BARBARO-GALTIERI, W. H. BARKAS, P. L. BASTIEN, J. KIRZ, and M. ROOS, *Reviews of Modern Physics,* Vol. 36, October, 1964. This tabulation of the known numerical data on particles has provided the material for Table 1 and Table 4.

A SELECTION OF SIGNIFICANT RESEARCH PAPERS

* MORRIS SHAMOS, *Great Experiments in Physics* (New York: Henry Holt and Company, 1959). This book contains annotated extracts (in

English) of many important papers—by Einstein, Planck, Thomson, Millikan, Rutherford, Bohr, Chadwick, and others.

* R. T. BEYER (ed.), *Foundations of Nuclear Physics* (New York: Dover Publications, Inc., 1949). Reprints of some fundamental papers, mostly from the early 1930's.

* J. J. THOMSON, "Cathode Rays," *Philosophical Magazine*, vol. 44, p. 293 (1897). A very readable paper on the discovery of the electron. Experiments are reported that convincingly show cathode rays to be beams of negatively charged particles. An annotated extract of this paper is to be found in Shamos, *Great Experiments in Physics* (above).

* E. RUTHERFORD and F. SODDY, "Radioactive Change," *Philosophical Magazine*, vol. 5, p. 576 (1903). This is the last of six papers published by Rutherford and Soddy in 1902 and 1903. In it they summarize evidence that radioactive change is a catastrophic subatomic transformation releasing vastly more energy per atom than chemical reactions.

ALBERT EINSTEIN, "On a Heuristic Point of View About the Emission and Absorption of Light," *Annalen der Physik*, vol. 17, p. 132 (1905). The photoelectric effect is explained with the help of the new photon concept. (In German.) An annotated excerpt, in English, is to be found in Morris Shamos, *Great Experiments in Physics* (above).

A. EINSTEIN, H. A. LORENTZ, H. MINKOWSKI, and H. WEYL, *The Principle of Relativity* (New York: Dover Publications, 1923). This book includes English translations of two of Einstein's famous 1905 papers on relativity, the first setting forth the idea of the relativity of time, the second predicting the equivalence of mass and energy. The papers appeared originally in *Annalen der Physik*. See also Shamos, *Great Experiments in Physics* (above).

* E. RUTHERFORD, "The Scattering of Alpha and Beta Particles by Matter and the Structure of the Atom," *Philosophical Magazine*, vol. 21, p. 669 (1911). The atom is revealed to be largely empty space with a small positively charged nucleus at its center. This paper is included in Beyer, *Foundations of Nuclear Physics* (above).

* NIELS BOHR, "On the Constitution of Atoms and Molecules," *Philosophical Magazine*, vol. 26, p. 1 (1913). The principle of the quantization of angular momentum is enunciated, the idea of the "quantum jump" is introduced, and the spectrum of the hydrogen atom is beautifully accounted for. See also Shamos, *Great Experiments in Physics* (above).

ARTHUR H. COMPTON, "A Quantum Theory of the Scattering of X-Rays by Light Elements," *Physical Review*, vol. 21, p. 483 (1923), and

"The Spectrum of Scattered X-Rays," *Physical Review*, vol. 22, p. 409 (1923). In the first paper Compton shows how the photon theory of X-ray deflection differs from the older classical wave theory. In the second paper he presents convincing experimental evidence for the photon picture of X-rays. Annotated extracts of these papers appear in Shamos, *Great Experiments in Physics* (above).

LOUIS DE BROGLIE, "A Tentative Theory of Light Quanta," *Philosophical Magazine*, vol. 47, p. 446 (1924). Despite its title, this paper is concerned also with a wave theory of material particles. Other papers by de Broglie (in French) presaging quantum mechanics are to be found in *Comptes Rendus* in 1923 and 1924.

N. BOHR, H. A. KRAMERS, and J. C. SLATER, "The Quantum Theory of Radiation," *Philosophical Magazine*, vol. 47, p. 785 (1924). One of the earliest papers to suggest that fundamental processes of nature are governed by laws of probability.

WOLFGANG PAULI, "On the Connection Between the Exclusion of Electron Groups in Atoms and the Complex Structure of Spectra," *Zeitschrift für Physik*, vol. 31, p. 765 (1925). The first formulation of the exclusion principle, that no two electrons can be in identically the same state of motion. (In German.)

WERNER HEISENBERG, "On the Quantum-Theoretical Interpretation of Kinematical and Mechanical Relationships," *Zeitschrift für Physik*, vol. 33, p. 879 (1925). The first presentation of the new quantum mechanics by the 24-year-old Heisenberg. (In German.)

* G. E. UHLENBECK and S. GOUDSMIT, "Spinning Electron and the Structure of Spectra," *Nature*, vol. 117, p. 264 (1926). An electron spin is postulated in order to explain various details of atomic structure.

ERWIN SCHRÖDINGER, "Quantization as an Eigenvalue Problem," *Annalen der Physik*, vol. 79, pp. 361 and 489 (1926). Quantum mechanics is developed as a wave theory. (In German.)

MAX BORN, "Quantum Mechanics of Collision Processes," *Zeitschrift für Physik*, vol. 38, p. 803 (1926). In this paper, Born proposes the probability interpretation of the newly discovered quantum mechanics. (In German.)

* CLINTON J. DAVISSON and LESTER H. GERMER, "Diffraction of Electrons by a Crystal of Nickel," *Physical Review*, vol. 30, p. 705 (1927). Demonstration of the wave nature of material particles.

W. HEISENBERG, "On the Essential Content of Quantum-Theoretical Kinematics and Mechanics," *Zeitschrift für Physik*, vol. 43, p. 172 (1927). The uncertainty principle is introduced. (In German.)

P. A. M. DIRAC, "The Quantum Theory of the Electron," *Proceedings of the Royal Society*, vol. A117, p. 610 (1928). Dirac successfully merged quantum mechanics and relativity in the "Dirac equation" that accounted for electron spin and predicted the existence of the positron.

WOLFGANG PAULI never published his historic suggestion of the neutrino. In December, 1930, he committed the idea to paper in a letter addressed to the "radioactive ladies and gentlemen" at a conference in Tübingen, Germany.* In that letter he wrote, "I don't trust myself at the moment to publish anything about this idea, so I first turn trustingly to you, dear radioactive friends . . . I admit that my way out might look rather improbable at first, since if the neutrino existed, it should have been seen long ago. But only he who takes risks can succeed."

* JAMES CHADWICK, "Possible Existence of a Neutron," *Nature*, vol. 129, p. 312 (1932). Experiments are described that strongly point to the existence of a new heavy neutral particle, the neutron.

WERNER HEISENBERG, "On the Structure of Atomic Nuclei," *Zeitschrift für Physik*, vol. 77, p. 1 (1932). Neutrons (just discovered) and protons are taken as the building blocks of nuclei in a theory that introduces the concept of isotropic spin and draws neutron and proton together as two manifestations of a single particle, the nucleon. (In German.)

* CARL D. ANDERSON, "The Apparent Existence of Easily Deflected Positives," *Science*, vol. 76, p. 238 (1932), and "The Positive Electron," *Physical Review*, vol. 43, p. 491 (1933). The first article presents the earliest evidence for the existence of the positron. The second provides further strong evidence. The second is included in Beyer, *Foundations of Nuclear Physics* (above).

ENRICO FERMI, "Attempt at a Theory of Beta Rays," *Zeitschrift für Physik*, vol. 88, p. 161 (1934). The hypothetical neutrino is incorporated into a successful theory of beta decay that postulates the creation and annihilation of material particles. (In German.) This paper is included in Beyer, *Foundations of Nuclear Physics* (above).

HIDEKI YUKAWA, "On the Interaction of Elementary Particles," *Proceedings of the Physico-Mathematical Society of Japan*, vol. 17, p. 48 (1935). A new particle, now called the pion, is predicted in order to account for the strong nuclear force between neutron and proton. This paper is included in Beyer, *Foundations of Nuclear Physics* (above).

* G. D. ROCHESTER and C. C. BUTLER, "Evidence for the Existence of

---

* I am indebted to Frederick Reines for bringing this letter to my attention and for supplying a copy of the original letter in German. In the excerpt given here, I use the word "neutrino," although Pauli used "neutron." Later it took both the neutron and the neutrino to fill the roles assigned to Pauli's postulated particle.

New Unstable Elementary Particles," *Nature*, vol. 160, p. 855 (1947). Discovery of the first "strange particles."

R. P. FEYNMAN, "Theory of Positrons," *Physical Review*, vol. 76, p. 749 (1949). A theory is developed in which positrons are treated as electrons moving backward in time.

* DONALD GLASER, "Bubble Chamber Tracks of Penetrating Cosmic Ray Particles," *Physical Review*, vol. 91, p. 762 (1953). First pictures and proof of the feasibility of the bubble chamber as a particle detector.

MURRAY GELL-MANN, "Isotopic Spin and New Unstable Particles," *Physical Review*, vol. 92, p. 833 (1953). The new law of strangeness conservation is proposed (but is not yet so named).

T. NAKANO and K. NISHIJIMA, "Charge Independence for V-Particles," *Progress of Theoretical Physics*, vol. 10, p. 581 (1953). An independent suggestion of the strangeness concept (not yet so named).

* DONALD GLASER, "Characteristics of Bubble Chambers," *Physical Review*, vol. 97, p. 474 (1955). Accumulated early evidence for the excellent potentiality of the bubble chamber.

* OWEN CHAMBERLAIN, EMILIO SEGRÈ, CLYDE WIEGAND, and THOMAS YPSILANTIS, "Observation of Antiprotons," *Physical Review*, vol. 100, p. 947 (1955). Discovery of the antiproton at Berkeley.

E. E. CHAMBERS and R. HOFSTADTER, "Structure of the Proton," *Physical Review*, vol. 103, p. 1454 (1956). Experiments are reported that reveal the distribution of electric charge within the proton.

C. N. YANG and T. D. LEE, "Question of Parity Conservation in Weak Interactions," *Physical Review*, vol. 104, p. 254 (1956). The first suggestion that the weak interactions might violate parity conservation, and proposed experimental tests.

* C. S. WU, E. AMBLER, R. W. HAYWARD, D. D. HOPPES, and R. P. HUDSON, "Experimental Test of Parity Conservation in Beta Decay," *Physical Review*, vol. 105, p. 1413 (1957). Report of the experiment with cobalt 60 (see pp. 224–226) proving that parity is not conserved in weak interactions.

R. L. GARWIN, L. M. LEDERMAN, and M. WEINRICH, "Observations of the Failure of Conservation of Parity and Charge Conjugation in Meson Decays: The Magnetic Moment of the Free Muon," *Physical Review*, vol. 105, p. 1415 (1957). Experimental proof that in pion decay the weak interactions violate two conservation laws.

M. GOLDHABER, L. GRODZINS, and A. W. SUNYAR, "Helicity of Neutrinos," *Physical Review*, vol. 109, p. 1015 (1958). Report of first experiment that proved the electron's neutrino to be left-handed.

* F. REINES, C. L. COWAN, JR., F. B. HARRISON, A. D. McGUIRE, and H. W. KRUSE, "Detection of the Free Antineutrino," *Physical Review*, vol. 117, p. 159 (1960). Presentation of conclusive evidence that the

electron's antineutrino exists as an elementary particle. (The first definite evidence was achieved by these workers several years earlier.)

R. V. Pound and G. A. Rebka, Jr., "Apparent Weight of Photons," *Physical Review Letters*, vol. 4, p. 337 (1960). Experimental proof that photons experience the gravitational interaction.

G. Danby, J.-M. Gaillard, K. Goulianos, L. M. Lederman, N. Mistry, M. Schwartz, and J. Steinberger, "Observation of High-Energy Neutrino Reactions and the Existence of Two Kinds of Neutrinos," *Physical Review Letters*, vol. 9, p. 36 (1962). Identification of the muon's neutrino and proof that it is distinct from the electron's neutrino.

* C. C. Giamati and F. Reines, "Experimental Test of the Conservation of Nucleons," *Physical Review*, vol. 126, p. 2178 (1962). The proton is shown to have a lifetime greater than 10^{26} years, providing a stringent test of baryon conservation.

* Ralph Shutt, Nicholas P. Samios, and thirty-one colleagues, "Observation of a Hyperon with Strangeness Minus Three," *Physical Review Letters*, vol. 12, p. 204 (1964). Discovery of the omega baryon.

Index

A Note about the Author

KENNETH W. FORD is Professor of Physics at the University of California, Irvine. This book was written while he was a National Science Foundation fellow working on a theory of heavy elementary particles at Imperial College, London.

Educated at the Phillips Exeter Academy and Harvard University, Professor Ford interrupted his graduate studies at Princeton University in 1950 to spend two years working on thermonuclear problems at Los Alamos and at Project Matterhorn in Princeton. He returned to Princeton University to receive his Ph.D. degree in 1953. Before going to the University of California in 1964, he was a member of the faculties of Indiana University and Brandeis University. In 1955–56, as a Fulbright fellow, he worked at the Max Planck Institut in Göttingen, Germany. Specializing in nuclear physics and particle physics, Professor Ford has published numerous papers in technical journals. A fellow of the American Physical Society, he has served on the Board of Editors of Physical Review.

tric ge	Antiparticle	No. of distinct particles	Average lifetime (seconds)	Typical mode of decay
al	same particle	1	infinite	—
al	same particle	1	infinite	—
al	$\overline{\nu}_e$	2	infinite	—
ive	e^+ (positron)	2	infinite	—
al	$\overline{\nu}_\mu$	2	infinite	—
ive	μ^+	2	2.20×10^{-6}	$\mu^- \rightarrow e^- + \overline{\nu}_e + \nu_\mu$
ve	π^- } same as the		2.55×10^{-8}	$\pi^+ \rightarrow \mu^+ + \nu_\mu$
ive	π^+ } particles	3	2.55×10^{-8}	$\pi^- \rightarrow \mu^- + \overline{\nu}_\mu$
al	π^0 }		1.8×10^{-16}	$\pi^0 \rightarrow \gamma + \gamma$
ve	$\overline{K^+}$ (negative)		1.23×10^{-8}	$K^+ \rightarrow \pi^+ + \pi^0$
al	$\overline{K^0}$	4	0.92×10^{-10} and^a	$K^0 \rightarrow \pi^+ + \pi^-$
al	same particle	1	6×10^{-8} more than 10^{-22}	$\eta \rightarrow \gamma + \gamma$
ve	$\overline{p}$ (negative)	4	infinite	—
al	$\overline{n}$		1013	$n \rightarrow p + e^- + \overline{\nu}_e$
al	$\overline{\Lambda^0}$	2	2.62×10^{-10}	$\Lambda^0 \rightarrow p + \pi^-$
ve	$\overline{\Sigma^+}$ (negative)		7.9×10^{-11}	$\Sigma^+ \rightarrow n + \pi^+$
ve	$\overline{\Sigma^-}$ (positive)	6	1.6×10^{-10}	$\Sigma^- \rightarrow n + \pi^-$
al	$\overline{\Sigma^0}$		about 10^{-20}	$\Sigma^0 \rightarrow \Lambda^0 + \gamma$
ve	$\overline{\Xi^-}$ (positive)		1.7×10^{-10}	$\Xi^- \rightarrow \Lambda^0 + \pi^-$
al	$\overline{\Xi^0}$	4	3×10^{-10}	$\Xi^0 \rightarrow \Lambda^0 + \pi^0$
ve	$\overline{\Omega^-}$ (positive)	$\dfrac{2}{36}$	about 10^{-10}	$\Omega^- \rightarrow \Xi^0 + \pi^-$